Eyes of Innocence

"We never look with eyes of innocence, we always look through our hopes, fears, thoughts and experiences. These form a wall in front of our eyes; a troubling like the ripples on a lake that distort our reflection of reality. Seldom do we look into the eyes of our fellow men and women, and when we do, we find ourselves stopped by this wall; but on a rare occasion we may meet someone and look into the eyes and to our surprise do not find ourselves stopped, but rather invited to enter into endless rolling fields and routes, vistas of innocent beauty."

Eyes of Innocence

*The complete interviews
taken for the documentary video
'A Fish in Search of Water'*

*"May we see not only with our two eyes,
but with the one eye which is our heart."
(Black Elk)*

Dona Holleman

Published by Pandion Enterprises

To order the video 'A Fish in Search of Water' (ISBN 90-805113-3-1)
you can send an e-mail to:
- pandion.usa@donaholleman.com (within USA)
- pandion@donaholleman.com (outside USA)

Or order the video at your local book shop.

Published by Pandion Enterprises
For more information: www.donaholleman.com
Lay out, cover design and photo editing by Walter Goyen,
Liqua Amersfoort (NL), www.liqua.nl
Photographs by Karina Eichner.
Printed in The Netherlands by Drukkerij Bariet, Ruinen.

ISBN 90-805113-4-X

Eyes of Innocence

THE INTERVIEWS

6   **Eyes of Innocence**
Dona Holleman

Preface One

by Diana Eichner
Director of the documentary film "A Fish in Search of Water"

I met Dona for the first time in 1997 in Berkeley, California. I was
beginning a four-year teacher training course with her, and I was eager
to learn as much yoga as I could absorb. The weeklong course gave
me enough information to work on my own for a whole year, but
there was an extra element in the teaching that I had not expected:
her use of images. She preferred the visual teaching to the verbal,
and she used powerful imagery to communicate her ideas. Instead
of explaining a yoga pose in a thousand words, she would say:
"Watch here!" She would do the pose, and then she would expect
the class to go ahead and do the same thing.

I quickly realized that to be able to learn from Dona, I had to stop
taking notes like a maniac and just watch her do her thing. I even
started to believe her when she said that, if I observed attentively,
the pose would jump from her body into my body through the eyes.

The technical aspect of the yoga poses was not all Dona wanted to
communicate. Her teaching was about the way we perceive the world
that is around us. The pose was the easy part; what was more difficult,
was letting go of one's ideas and preconceptions and opening oneself
to a new kind of experience. One which is not limited to yoga poses
practiced indoors. It is the experience of perceiving everything with
attention: from animals and nature to films and TV.

Dona would use the most amazing visual metaphors to explain her
ideas. One day she would talk about the way dolphins jump over
the water, and not just above the water like humpback whales do;

and the next day she would talk about the way Douglas Fairbanks jumped in the 1920's Hollywood classic El Zorro. The possibilities are infinite, as long as everything is perceived with equal attention.

Dona's vivid metaphors stayed with me long after that first week, and the internalized images became my teachers. Something had really jumped through the eyes into my mind, and it had stayed there. Dona's creative use of images inspired me to think visually, and that is when I started to imagine a film...

Preface Two

by Katherine Rabinowitz.
Producer of the documentary film "Eyes of Innocence"

I started studying with Dona in 1993, attending retreats and beginning a series of teachers seminars in Berkeley. Her teaching changed my practice and my whole view of yoga after studying for years previously. Returning to the States after a retreat with Dona in Italy, I would reconnect with the work by following her yoga syllabus, reading Jyotim and her other books. I began to wish for some kind of a film to remember her techniques, not only the poses, but also a way to envision the inspiration I felt from her being and her verbal teaching.

When Diana Eichner approached me after the second year of the teachers' course in Berkeley with an idea for a film, I thought it must be the right time and the right person to work with. Dona was open and willing to undertake the project then as well. Films are their own mysteries, a form that emerges from a composite of concept and image, knowledge and experience. They begin when something says go, and so we all started in.

Diana came to visit me in New York, and we brainstormed and practiced together for several days. We watched other yoga videos to see what we didn't need to duplicate. We watched uncut interviews with Dona, and our husbands gave their more objective views and asked hard questions about our fledgling ideas. I wasn't sure to what degree I could become involved, since I had one and three year-old children, who were also demanding of time, and I was loving being a mother.

I knew it could become a big commitment. I had worked on film
and television productions in some form or other since 1985. I had
also worked extensively in the non-profit sector, from both the
grant-making and grant-writing sides. With Diana as producer and
director for the hands-on components of the film, we sent treat-
ments back and forth by e-mail, and I began to work on securing
funding. I arranged for LTV, a local public-access cable TV station
where I had worked for several years, to be a non-profit vehicle for
the project with its 501(c)-3 status. I began writing fundraising
letters and proposals and circulating them. Several substantial initial
donations have been generated, and we have high hopes of more to
come.

I am eagerly awaiting a look at the footage of Dona at Jackson Hole,
and am excited to see the first cut. I loved hearing from Diana about
filming there. It's a time of great anticipation, and knowing much
hard work is still to come. Working on this film is a particular
privilege for me, because it's another way of working with Dona,
one that I hope will bring her light and depth to others who may not
know her, or about yoga. I think our collective wish is that the film
should open possibilities of inner growth to others, to see themselves in new ways, as it has already for us.

Interview indoors at Clymer House

DIANA » Why do you think that human beings need to create systems that explain the world?

DONA » We create systems that try to explain something that is basically unexplainable. As human beings we have to live in this world, we have to function in this world. Thus we have to create a certain order, a certain structure in which everyone knows the rules, and these rules differ from country to country, from culture to culture, from language to language, from religious society to religious society. These rules form a certain structure and we use the structure in order to not only create a belief system, but also to create a way of being able to function together, to communicate together.

DIANA » Do they interfere with our perception of reality?

DONA » I think that they interfere with our perception of reality. A newborn child does not have language, it does not have words, and it does not have the structure that an adult has. As the child gets older the parents begin to give it a language, a structure. The child sees something and the parents say: "This is daddy." The child sees something else and the parents say: "This is mommy." Thus gradually the range of labels, the range of words increases and the child begins to learn to differentiate between all the different objects and to give each object a name. As time passes and the person goes through various experiences these names begin to collect memories, associations. For instance, if a child would see a fire for the first time it would not know what to do with it. It might put its hand on the fire and get burned. The name fire, the object fire, and the memory of being burned get then mixed together and stored in the memory. The next time the child sees a fire the name, the memory, the association and the burning feeling come back and it will not put the hand on the fire again. Therefore in certain ways it is good, in others it is interfering. It always interferes with perception; the association, the memory, the word always interferes and we have to learn how to deal with the interference.

DIANA » How do we deal with the interference?

DONA » We deal with the interference in the first place by being aware that we make the structure, the human structure, and that in this way we build a world within the world, as it were. In the Middle Ages people thought that the earth was the center of the universe, until Galileo discovered that that was not true at all. He discovered that the earth was rotating around the sun, and not the sun around the earth. This was a huge revolution. He found out that our solar system rotates around the sun, and that probably the sun rotated in space around other systems, that everything is rotating and on the move. Thus this whole idea of a fixed earth with fixed values evaporated, it had to be put to the side and changed into a different view. On the earth each species of animals does exactly that, like in the Middle Ages, it puts itself in the center of the universe, of creation. Thus an elk looks at the world from an elk-centric point of view, everything relates to the elk. A fox looks at the world from a fox-centric point of view.

DIANA » Dona, do you want to talk about chaos?

DONA » This movie is about yoga, about human beings, about the world we live in, about how we in a way create our own world and then get trapped in this worldview that we ourselves create. I am very interested in what modern science says about the universe and the quantum world. Quantum physics is especially interesting, because they are finding now that what we conceive of as our universe and our way of life is in reality our own creation in the most literal sense. There is a quantum world dealing with particles and waves and atoms and now they are even saying that these particles or waves are not things in themselves but exist more in the realm of probabilities, possibilities, of a possible happening. They are happenings more than things. The world of things that we perceive is actually a world of happenings, not of real things. These happenings are something that we cannot know because our nervous system cannot filter it, cannot really understand it. According to modern sciences the whole universe of this quantum web is based on ten or eleven dimensions, while human beings function only within four dimensions: space and time. This was what Einstein found out: that human beings live in a four dimensional world. What the scientists are now saying is that there are eleven dimensions out there. Something has programmed animals and trees and human beings to create its own little four-dimensional corner within this vast structure of eleven dimensions which are based on tension, on possibilities, on probabilities more than on actual things. In this vast structure each living thing - and I think it includes trees and plants - creates its own world, its own perception. This perception differs from species to species and is based on the needs of the particular species. For instance, snakes who have a very poor eyesight can see through the tongue, detect body heat and thus can zoom in on the mouse or the rat. An eagle on the other hand flies very high and so his eyesight is about six times the strength of our eyesight to see the mouse in the grass. Each species creates its own world with its senses, with the combination of its senses, and it functions within that world.

Nature has created an enormous amount of species throughout the evolution of the earth and for each species that comes along it makes a new 'program'. Most animals go probably on automatic pilot, which we as human beings call 'instinct'. Animals function according to instincts and probably have little choice in being aware of these instincts or doing something about them. A wolf cannot get up one morning and say: "I want to become a vegetarian and eat grass;" he is bound to his wolf nature, his hunting nature, his meat eating nature. On the other hand a moose cannot get up one morning and say: "I want to start hunting wolves." The moose cannot do that; it is stuck in his moose-centric view of the world, as the wolf is stuck in his wolf-centric view of the world or the elk in his elk-centric view of the world. Human beings do the same thing; they also have a view of the world, a homo-centric point of view. When some of the great ape tribes mutated and became human the first stage they went through was called 'Homo erectus', which means 'upright human', because he got from the four-legged position into the two-legged position with the pelvis hinging around the femur heads. It took a long time to go through evolution to get this new skeleton into a better state to become real human.

DIANA » Does our perception as humans relate to our necessities as a species?

D O N A » Exactly. We belong in the prey category, we are not originally hunters or meat eaters but leaf eaters; the body is from a leaf eating stock. The body itself has the memory of being hunted and that already clouds our perception. It makes us see the world in a certain way. As human beings we also need to live in a world where everything has inborn defensive tools like horns, or hooves, or teeth. For the human being nature had a new idea. It said: "This little thing has nothing to defend itself with, nothing to help it survive, so let him have something new." This new thing was the frontal brain. Because of the frontal brain we are a little more complicated than the animals because we still have the animal body with its fears, its memories, its instincts, its automatic pilot situation; but in the automatic pilot situation we have now also a little person who can switch the automatic pilot off at will which animals do not have. That makes it very complicated.

D I A N A » But that brain also makes us fall into the trap of thinking that our perception of the world is the same as the world itself.

D O N A » Exactly. The aim of the brain was to make humans survive against all odds, because all the odds were against us. The brain was a tool in order to survive and it is very young, about a million and a half years old, while the body is hundreds of millions of years old. The brain, being very young, has the excitement and the presumption of a young thing which means that it thinks that whatever it comes up with that is the final thing, the real thing. The brain creates the human structure, a human corner in the universe like every animal does, but we have that extra possibility of changing which animals do not have. Though we have that possibility that does not mean that we always use it. In fact, most of the time we do not use that possibility. We are always placing our human structure in the center of the universe, which every animal does. An elk can only be an elk and is the center of the world as an elk; in the same way a wolf is the center of the world as a wolf, human beings are also the center of the world as human beings. In the Middle Ages people thought that the earth was standing still and all the planets were rotating around the earth. That idea got changed when they found out that the earth was rotating around the sun. Then they thought that the sun was standing still and everything was rotating around the sun. That idea too became obsolete. Then they found out that everything was rotating around everything else, that the whole universe, the whole cosmos was rotating. On the human level we still live in the idea of the Middle Ages idea that the human mind is like the earth and everything rotates around it, that we as human beings are the final thing in nature and that our way of seeing the world is the real thing. We do not realize that this is arbitrary and that we too are caught in a homo-centric view of the world in the same way as a wolf is in a wolf-centric and the elk in an elk-centric view.

DIANA » What are the consequences of our thinking of ourselves as separate from the universe?

DONA » The consequence of creating a homo-centric worldview and then being trapped in it is that we loose touch with everything else. In the first place we are caught in a way of looking at the universe and seeing the universe that is limited. In the second place it shuts us out from everything else. In the third place it misleads us. We get trapped in a way of seeing that has to do with a structure that we ourselves create. Modern science says that the universe is chaos. Chaos actually means the un-structured, the un-manifested universe. Because we need to function, we need to live, we have to create within that un-structured universe a structure which is typical human so that we can communicate with each other. This is the structure that we create and then we believe is the real thing. This has to do with language, with belief systems, with our own needs and fears as human beings.

DIANA » It is man-made?

DONA » It is a man-made structure and within that man-made structure we function. This is OK; we need to make a man-made world. We need to have a house, we need to have a car to drive to the office, we need to eat, we also need certain ideas, certain beliefs. The problem starts when we create this man-made structure and then we are trapped in it. We forget that there is a whole universe beyond the structure, that the structure is only a very thin film superimposed on the vastness out there and that this film is only for practical purposes. We get trapped in it.

DIANA » Why do men feel they need this structure?

DONA » We need the structure, we are supposed to have one. We have our senses and with those senses we create a certain worldview that is inbuilt in human beings. If you compare human beings with other animals then you can see that each animal has a different range of senses and therefore a different input from outside. This chaos outside, this un-differentiated universe, tickles the senses of every species. The senses are like filtering tubes that bring that tickling sensation, that information from outside into the nervous system of the species. Depending on the openings of the nervous system like the eyes, the ears, the tongue, and depending on the way they function, the nervous system of that species will then process that tickling from outside and create that particular view, that particular world. Human beings also have the five senses of information: the eyes, the ears, the nose, the tongue, and the skin. Compared to most animals these senses are pretty limited. Our eyes can never do what an eagle eye can do; our ears cannot hear what dogs can hear. But for our purpose they were apparently sufficient. As that un-differentiated universe outside touches the senses, that information, that touch is brought inward and then the mind, the brain creates that worldview. We see trees, we see animals, we see colors because of the tickling from outside being put together into a coherent picture. That picture is our human version of the universe. The problem is that we think that the human version of the universe is the real thing, the total thing. We forget that like every animal our view, our picture inside, is also only a fraction of what is out there. It is not at all the whole thing. But we get trapped in the idea that our man-made world, our human world, is the complete picture. That is the first mistake because it places us automatically outside nature, outside the whole of the universe; it makes us think that we are above nature, above the universe, because we are caught in the idea that the human version of the universe is the real thing. Within that human-centric worldview which depends on the programming that we have been given as human beings - the programming of the nervous system - each culture, each country, creates again a smaller room. Within the bigger house of the human world each culture makes a room and thus narrows it further down. From the un-differentiated universe we narrow it down to the human-centric world, the homo-centric view and then to the culture-centric view. The rooms get smaller and smaller and the space around us gets smaller and smaller. You become a German, you become a Jew, you become a Frenchman, you become an American because you build a little cocoon around yourself that says: "I'm an American." It is like a cocoon and we forget that this cocoon is purely man-made, purely arbitrary and has no connection with reality.

ᴅ ɪ ᴀ ɴ ᴀ » It makes us feel safe?

ᴅ ᴏ ɴ ᴀ » It creates a safety zone on the one hand and on the other it creates a dangerous situation. If you look at Europe you see all these different countries. They have waged wars since centuries and thousands of people have died for wars between France and England and Germany and Austria. But the birds migrating from Scandinavia to Africa will fly over all those countries and never know whether they are flying over Germany or Austria or Italy. All they know is that they are flying over land. The borderlines - German, Italian, French - are man-made words and man-made divisions. On the one hand these create a diversity of cultures and languages that is fun, but on the other hand it also creates instability where culture is pitted against culture. If the situation gets very unstable you have war because one culture wants to get the supremacy over the other.

ᴅ ɪ ᴀ ɴ ᴀ » How do we go beyond the structure that we create as a culture?

D O N A » The structure is not only cultural. Within the cultural structure we make more and more boxes: within the big box of the universe we make a human box and then we make a culture box and within the culture we make religious boxes. In America there are Catholics and Protestants and Lutherans, all these different religious boxes, and within the religious boxes you make still smaller boxes. This endless fragmentation is done for safety zone reasons. As long as I 'know' that I am an American or a Catholic I feel safe because I know that I have other people around me who think in the same way and do the same thing. We do not realize that it is a phantom safety zone. Thus this whole fragmentation is a form of unawareness, a form of ignorance, a desire to belong to a certain group. The only way to stop this fragmentation is by attention, by awareness, to be aware of the whole process of compartmentalization, of fragmentation. This does not mean that we have to get rid of the fragmentation. We need the man-made world to function as people, but the problem begins when we get caught in it to the point that we believe deeply in it. It is OK to be an American but if you take the word 'American' and the concept 'American' as a real thing, not as a phantom, arbitrary thing, then it becomes a problem. Therefore the crux of the matter is to learn to be in two places at the same time: on the one hand to function and live as an American in America in a man-made world, but on the other hand to also be perfectly aware that it is a phantom situation, not a real one, and so we do not get caught. We use it, we function in it, but we do not get caught.

D I A N A » We do not take our fantasy too seriously?

D O N A » We know it is a fantasy, that we live in fantasyland. We create all these fantasylands in order to make our world but we should never lose sight of the fact that it is like going to Disney Land. You know it is all pretense. It is fun but you have to be aware that it is pretense and not take it too seriously, otherwise it will condition your being, condition your reactions to the world.

D I A N A » Do you think this awareness is a revolutionary idea?

DONA » The idea that we actually live in two worlds at the same time is not revolutionary, it is not a new idea. People have been aware of this from the beginning but only on a small scale, only the 'elect'. The interesting thing in our time is that we now have the possibility to make this awareness mainstream. In the old days it was only a few mystic people who understood that the man-made world was a trap, a vortex in which people got caught and circled around. Now, because of science probing deeper and deeper into the universe and into the universe of particle science, science itself is opening the door for everybody - for the lay people, for the people in the street - to get into a different state of mind where they can understand that we do it all ourselves. And doing it all ourselves we can also stop the show.

DIANA » Is science not another fantasy? How can fantasy take us out of fantasy?

DONA » Science is also fantasy and that is very obvious to science itself because each theory that is developed is declared obsolete twenty years later and is replaced by another theory. The universe is something that is ultimately unknowable by human beings. If it is coiled in eleven dimensions how can our nervous system, our brain, our body, which are caught in four dimensions, contain the understanding of eleven dimensions? There is no way that a four dimensional thing can contain eleven dimensions. That would be like a matchbox containing a house. A matchbox cannot contain a house. The house can contain a matchbox but the matchbox cannot contain a house. This universe, this vast universe, can contain the human version but not the other way around. I think that once you understand that then you can say: "OK, this is the way we are and the only way of dealing with that is to understand that we do it ourselves. Therefore if you can suspend everything for a moment you might get a glimpse of the fact that there is something out there that we will never understand. That in itself is the revolution, it is the mystical experience in itself.

DIANA » So it is not 'knowing', but a glimpse?

DONA » It is a glimpse. What we understand by 'knowing', is to contain something in language. Language has to do with structuring. When a baby is born it does not have language. It has the senses and with them it perceives a world for which it has no names. Gradually the names are added to everything, the names or the labels are put together with the things out there and the baby begins to get a structured world in which everything has a name. It gets caught in language. This language, the naming of the thing, the naming of whatever you see, is necessary in order to give it continuity. If I would see a tree and I would not have a name for the tree, the next time I see a tree it would be a new experience again. But by giving it a name I can carry it through time.

DIANA » Is it part of that cultural fragmentation to explain the world through language?

DONA » It is explaining the world through language forgetting that language itself is four-dimensional. Because language consists words that have been pasted - as it were - on things its content is always four-dimensional, caught in space and time. Language has to do with space but also with time. Time has two aspects: there is chronological time and there is psychological time. Chronological time is the ticking of the clock, the seasons coming and going. Psychological time is the human structure. The human structure is also contained in chronological time but our awareness of the human structure takes place in psychological time. I carry the world from one day to the next through the medium of language, which is memory with its associations.

DIANA » Something we impose on the world.

DONA » The whole thing is an imposition. It is like having the whole window, the whole nature outside, and you impose a film on it that you have painted. You paint a picture and then superimpose that over the window, so you see what is out there through something that you have superimposed on it, which is language, which is structure, the human structure.

DIANA » Going back to the systems that fragment and create safety zones. Can yoga be misunderstood as one of these systems?

DONA » Any time you have a word you have a system, whether the system is an orthodox religion or philosophy or yoga. The moment you have the word 'yoga', you have again a box within the box. It is the Chinese egg within the egg. Yoga is again an egg within the totality of the universe that says: if you do this then you have a certain result, like all the religions, all the philosophies. It is a system, which was meant to help people to get out of the system, let us say. Paradoxically enough all religions and philosophies are systems to help people to jump out of the systems into this mystical experience, but it is a paradox that simply does not work because the system, including yoga, has to do with language, with chronological time, with psychological time. There is no way to go from a linear, psychological and chronological time pathway into a state of mind where there is no time, no future. It is an either/or situation. You can use a system like yoga to become healthy, to have a better quality of life. It can have a lot of nice side effects. But to use yoga as a system of reaching a state where time has no longer any meaning is not possible.

DIANA » How can we reach that state then?

DONA » That is the million-dollar question. How can you reach the timeless state? By stopping time. Again I take an example from quantum physics. In quantum physics there is a term - which now is a mainstream term - which is the 'quantum leap'. Many people have a hazy idea of what the quantum leap is. It is not a little particle sort of leaping from one place to another. That is not it. The quantum leap is when a particle is in a certain state and then simply disappears out of that state and appears in another state. It has nothing to do with a leap through space or time. It simply disappears here and appears there, as by magic. The only way to go from the state of psychological time to the timeless state is exactly that -

by a quantum leap. We are now learning that human beings have two possibilities and maybe we are different from the animals in that way. We have a mind which functions in time and space, which makes the man-made structure, the man-made world, and functions in that. But we also have the mind that can make that quantum leap, disappear out of the continuous mind and appear in a state of mind where it is outside the man-made structure, outside the man-made function, outside psychological time, though not out of chronological time.

The first 'mind' is called 'the continuous mind' and functions automatically in chronological time, but creates also psychological time through its structure, through its interpretation of the universe. The other 'mind' is the 'wild mind', the untamed, undomesticated mind, the 'quantum mind' which is not caught in the man-made structure and which therefore can see whatever is filtered through the eyes and the ears without the imposition of the man-made structure. That is what we call 'the eyes of innocence', the 'Eyes of Innocence', because those eyes, seeing the world like that, do not alter it with ideas.

DIANA » One cannot follow a system to reach that quantum leap?

DONA » No. Systems are caught in time, in practice, and thus cannot make the quantum leap. Systems may be good for laying a certain type of groundwork, but I am not even sure how much groundwork you can lay. Through yoga or through other systems you can get healthy, you can get less worried about things, less distracted. But you cannot make that quantum jump from the continuous mind to the quantum mind. In quantum physics they say that a photon, or any particle, has two possibilities, it can manifest as a wave or as a particle. From a wave it cannot become a particle, and a particle cannot become a wave. What happens is that one of the two possibilities 'collapses'. Either the wave function 'collapses' or the particle function 'collapses'. Thus the other one is automatically there.

DIANA » We were talking about the possibility of being in both places at the same time.

DONA » In the totality of the universe - if there is a totality - every species has its own little corner, its own little world, and as human beings we have to live in our world. We have no choice. We have to be human and live in a human world and as such you might as well participate fully in it. The difficulty is when we believe that that view is the real thing. In reality it is only a man-made show that we ourselves create. We are meant to create it and to participate in it. However, if you believe that the show is the real thing then it becomes a vortex in which you get caught and that is how all the suffering and the problems arise. Because we cannot get out of it. A vortex is one of these things that you get into very fast but it is very difficult to get out of. By birth we get into the vortex of human life, of human existence, of the human structure and it is very difficult to get out of it. There is a way, though, of being aware that we are caught in a vortex, that we are caught in a human way of being, in a human society, and that we have the choice of either playing the game, playing the show while believing in it, or playing the show knowing that it is only a show. It is the awareness that it is only a show that makes you free. Free to play the game, to play the show, to play it fully, but at the same time to know that it is only a show and not to be caught in it. That is meant with living in the two worlds.

DIANA » If you have that awareness, then the conflicts between Catholics and Protestants would stop.

DONA » Those conflicts are totally idiotic because they are based on nothing, on absolutely nothing. They are based only on ideas, not on something real, substantial. The man-made structure has a lot of potentiality, a lot of possibilities, and we have to play the game, but we can also keep, as it were, the balance between playing the game and not being a part of the game. Thus we do not take it too seriously. We play it but we do not take it too seriously.

DIANA » Bringing this back to yoga. What would be a real way of teaching yoga without prescribing a system that will lead us back into ideas?

DONA » You can only 'teach' a method. You teach a method that you hope will bring the student to a different state of mind. A teacher occupies an impossible place. In the first place, in order to teach somebody else or to help somebody else you would have to be that other person. How do you know what the other person needs or can take or understand? Teaching is always interference from outside into somebody's inner structure. You cannot know whether you are hitting the target or not; there is no way of knowing that. Therefore it is very dangerous. Teaching and helping are very dangerous. You can help on a superficial level, giving bread and butter to somebody or clothes to the poor, things like that, but if you come closer into psychological help or even philosophical help then you get into quicksand because you do not know where the other person is in his life experience. The only way to teach is to just do it yourself, to do the quantum leap yourself. Then you are like a mirror for the other person to see that you can deal with you own hypnosis - because this whole thing of the man-made structure is a profound hypnosis that is imposed on human beings from birth onward. The human structure, the Catholic structure, the Protestant structure, the Jewish structure, the German structure, all these structures are a form of hypnosis. We are caught in the hypnosis and cannot get out of it. Thus the only way of teaching is to show that you can get out of it. Then the other person, seeing that, can look inside him or herself and see the same kind of hypnosis and know that there is a way out. But you cannot interfere in the hypnosis of another; you cannot stop the other hypnosis. You cannot do that; only the person himself can do that.

DIANA » You were talking about words.

DONA » It is very interesting. On the one hand, each culture creates a language structure, which is useful in that culture and which has meaning within that culture. Then it kind of flips around and the language structure begins to conditions us within that culture. For instance, if you have a culture that deals ten months out of the year with snow, like the Eskimo's and the northern Scandinavian countries, it has many words for snow. These people have to hunt to get their food so they have to know about snow, thin snow, thick snow, new snow, old snow. They have many different words for each type and particular condition of snow so that they know the situation, whether to go out or whether to stay in. In tropical countries there may not be any word for snow at all because there is no snow, but there may be many different words for 'palm tree' for which in an Eskimo country or a northern country there probably would not be any word because there are no palm trees in the northern countries. Each culture has its own language, its own words, and then these words begin to condition you. If an Eskimo would use a particular word for a particularly dangerous type of snow he would stay home; but if a tropical person would go there and hear that word it would not have any meaning and so he might go out and die. Each culture creates its language and then that language turns around and conditions us. Suppose I am born and raised in a strictly Christian culture and I see a building, which is a church, and then I see another building which is maybe a casino or just a house. For me the first building is sacred and the second is secular. But again, like in the case of the birds flying over the country, suppose there is a mouse looking for food. It may go into the church or into the casino building. For him it is exactly the same; it is just a place with potential food inside. Or if there are cracks in the floor the grass will grow both in the church building as in the casino building, it does not make any difference. The feeling that we should be careful and talk in hushed tones in the church and can shout and yell in the casino building is arbitrary, man-made. It conditions us in the way that we have programmed language. First we have a thing, then we have the language, and then the language programs us. It is a kind of circular dance.

DIANA » You mentioned looking at the world with religious eyes. Those religious eyes would be to not differentiate between the casino and the church?

DONA » Saying to look at the world with religious eyes is misleading if you take the word 'religious' in the modern sense. 'Religious' comes from re-ligere in Latin. The Latin verb means 'to tie again'. You want to tie yourself again to the universe, not to the man-made world. That would be the original meaning of 'religious'. Like the word 'intelligence' which means 'to tie inside'. That is the original meaning of intelligence, to connect inside. Religion is to connect again with what is out there. This movie is called 'Eyes of Innocence', which is less dense than 'religious eyes'. 'Innocent' comes from the Latin verb 'nocere', which means 'to harm', so innocence means 'harmless'. We create language and then language turns around and creates us or conditions us so that when we look at things we 'harm' them. We harm them because we do not look at the things in themselves but we look at the things with our memories and associations. It is like a puddle and the ripples on the puddle, or a lake: the lake reflects the stars, the sunlight, the trees, there is a clear reflection. To look at the world like that would be to look with religious or innocent eyes: the reflection is not distorted, it is not changed, it is not harmed. But if you throw a stone in the lake it makes ripples. These ripples are our associations, our memories, our doings, and in that way we distort the reflection in the puddle, we 'harm' the reflection. It is no longer a pure reflection, a clean reflection, but it is pulled out of its clarity. This is what we do all the time. We look at the world, we look at the universe through the ripples so we never see the clear image, the clear reflection.

DIANA » If we take the ripples away we might let the world come to us?

DONA » We cannot take the ripples away. The only thing you can do is to be aware that the ripples distort the image. Anything you do to take the ripples away will make more ripples because you are acting still in time and space. The only thing we can do is to be aware that we make the ripples. That very awareness, that attention to the fact that we make ripples is already the quantum leap. The interesting thing is that awareness or attention is already a quantum leap in itself. There is no way to 'become aware', to 'become attentive'. You can either be aware or not be aware, but you cannot 'become' it.

DIANA » Thus learning yoga and sitting in meditation for hours will not take us to that place where there are no ripples.

DONA » Doing meditation, whether it is yogi meditation or other types of meditation, is still a process in time and a process in time will never take you across the gap which the quantum leap does because you are still continuing in time. In the time process you have a goal and you are working your way towards the goal. In yoga it may be enlightenment or bliss or nirvana or whatever. The moment you have a word for your goal you know what that goal is. The moment you know what the goal is it cannot be the real thing because knowledge is within the four-dimensional structure of our human existence, while the real thing is not. There is a story of the monkey on the hand of the Buddha. The monkey was boasting and saying: "Oh I'm going to jump here, I'm going to get off the hand, I'm going to fly in the universe..." The Buddha said: "Go ahead, go and jump." The monkey jumped, and jumped, and jumped, but every time he jumped he still landed on the hand of the Buddha. It is only by stopping to jump that we can fall off the hand of the Buddha. That is the quantum leap. Whatever you do, whether it is meditation, or chanting, or yoga you are still sitting on the hand of the Buddha.

DIANA » We were talking about hypnosis... what words and language do to our minds.

DONA » We are caught in two types of hypnosis. The first one is inbuilt in the human structure. It is the hypnosis that forces us to perceive an actual material world. When I touch my body or a chair or anything else I experience it as hard and when I hit my hand on the wall it hurts. According to quantum physics this is a strange situation because basically objects - including my own body and walls and chairs - exist because they are built out of atoms. An 'atom' in the Greek language means something that cannot be cut further: 'a- tomos'. It was supposed to be the final little building block of the universe. This has proven to be a mistake. In fact the atom has been cut into further bits and pieces, the neutrons, the protons, the electrons, the particles. But basically all objects are made of atoms. If you blow up an atom to the size of the cathedral in Rome then the actual material part of it is the size of a grain of sand. Thus the body is built of things that are practically nothing, that are almost wholly empty space. The body, the chairs, things consist of atoms that in reality are - for the most part - empty space. The million dollar question therefore is: "Why do I experience the body and other things as so dense that I can hit against them, that I touch them and feel them and I get hurt when I bang into them?" This is the primary hypnosis that we live under, that we are forced somehow by nature to experience the world of atoms as something solid. It is somehow a maddening thought that when I do a position or I walk or when I do something with my body and I hit myself against the wall or burn myself with fire that something that is nothing can get hurt by something else that is nothing. This is a maddening thought in itself. That is the primary inbuilt hypnosis in which we are caught. On top of that we build a language hypnosis that conditions us to the extent that we have waged wars for untold centuries to defend things that in reality exist only as ideas. The hypnosis of language is our belief systems: the belief that the church is sacred and the casino is not. In the last two world wars the bombers were told beforehand to spare the cathedrals and the artwork of the cities and just get on with bombing houses and people. This is the extreme end of hypnosis, that certain things are sacred and precious and other things are not sacred and precious including human beings. This is the final tragic result of conditioning and hypnosis.

DIANA » To get out of this hypnosis, of ideas that fragment the world into this-is-good and this-is-bad is in final analysis our own responsibility as human beings. How do we assume this responsibility?

DONA » We have to be aware that we are conditioned, that we are hypnotized and that this conditioning is a double-edged sword. On the one hand it is good because we have a coherent structure to our world, but on the other hand it can be very dangerous and damaging. Each of us has the responsibility of being aware of this problem.

DIANA » Are we responsible ourselves or do we project that responsibility onto a teacher?

DONA » The first hypnosis that forces us as human beings to perceive a four-dimensional solid world is necessary. It is something we cannot get out from. The other one, the one of language, we can get out of. We can learn to walk the tightrope where, on the one hand, we are aware of creating a world that conditions our way of thinking, but on the other hand also be out of that. Nobody can do that for you. Each person has the responsibility to be aware of his or her own hypnosis, the way you perceive the world and to be responsible for switching, of making that quantum leap into the other mind, the mind where you know that you are dealing with man-made values, man-made conditionings and at the same time not be conditioned by them. As a teacher you cannot do that for another. A teacher should never interfere with the other person. The problem in teaching or helping is in the first place that you place yourself above the other person. This is a presumptuous position to be in, to be in a position where you think that you know what the other person needs and what kind of help you can give. In the second place each human being is totally on his own, there is no way for anyone of us to even know what the other one is seeing. I do not know what other people see or hear. I may be seeing pink elephants and somebody else may call them green trees. I do not know what other people see or hear, let alone what they think or feel. In that kind of darkness to see if you can help somebody else is to say the least unrealistic. To effectively help somebody else you have to be the other person, but you are not, you are yourself. Thus the only thing a teacher can do in all honesty is stop calling himself a teacher and just do his own thing. Also many people become teachers or do other activities involving other people in order to get away from themselves, unconsciously. It is much easier to 'fix' someone else than to fix your own problem. Therefore, the first thing you have to do is stop calling yourself a teacher or a helper and just do your own thing, watch your own hypnosis, watch your own conditioning, watch how you are moving in a very small circle and see if by awareness, by being attentive to that you can just open the windows of your own mind. That is the only way for another person to learn from you. Because you learn by seeing somebody else, not by getting imposed on, not by getting spoon-fed. Spoon-feeding never teaches anything. The only way we learn is by saying: "Hey, yeah, somebody else can do it, I can also do it." Which means that the full responsibility of the person is on himself, on herself. Each person has to deal with his own mind, with his own point in life, in the culture where he is. You cannot do it for another.

Eyes of Innocence
Dona Holleman

2   Interview indoors at Clymer House, photo looking session

DONA » When I was somewhere in my twenties, I read a book by a journalist which became one of my favorite books. The journalist was Charles Fort and he lived at the end of the 19th and the beginning of the 20th century. He collected all kinds of pieces of journalistic material from magazines and scientific journals. They were strange articles about things like frogs falling out of the sky. He wanted really to think through things and not just accept them.

I remember in particular one story about red rain falling out of the sky. On the one hand Charles Fort gave the official explanation of the scientists saying that it was sand from the Sahara that was picked up by a whirlwind, mixed with the rain and then dumped on England. Then he made his own theory, saying that it was a dragon that flew over and somebody had hit the dragon with an arrow and it was dripping blood. Then he began to defend both explanations, both views so well that in the end you do not believe either one.

T O N I » You do not know which one to believe.

D O N A » Therefore you just say: "OK, any explanation is fine. We are back to the turtles in the turtle story." In my life I went through a lot of extremes. If you go through a lot of extremes then in the end you come to a more central position. I began life in a very extreme position, in a Japanese concentration camp in Bangkok, and from there I moved to a castle in Holland. Going from prison to a castle where there was a Quaker school. I went from a prison to a castle, from a Buddhist country to a Christian setup. So already you get these extremes balancing against each other. I think that the wider the distance is the easier it is to come to a central position. From the Quaker school we moved to Indonesia, so by the time I was twenty-two, twenty-three years old I had gone through four major religions: Buddhism, Christianity, Islam and Hinduism. In the end that makes it easier to take distance from every one and say: "OK, everyone has something and in the end each one is only a system for safety, for feeling conformable, for feeling that you belong to something."

Going through a whole lifetime we come back to the time element, that psychological time is very flexible. For instance, I left Indonesia when I was thirteen years old and when I left, I was heartbroken. I was really upset about leaving my house and my city. When I came back thirty years later to that house and to the school where I used to go it was as if I had been there only yesterday, that I had gone to school yesterday; it was as if nothing had happened in between.

There was no time lapse, even though thirty years had passed. This shows you how time can really stretch and condense according to psychological needs. And going back to Indonesia I also realized something else, which is that you absorb through the eyes and through the senses and store it somewhere in your body. It may come out years later and you do not realize where it comes from because you have forgotten the original circumstances.

D O N A » This photograph is the island of Bali. We were talking about chaos, the universe, the 'wildness' of the universe. Within the 'wildness' of nature in Bali human beings have made a little oasis and this oasis is what feeds them, rice, fruit, etc. But it is only an oasis in the wildness, in the chaos of the wild nature: within the wild woods of Bali a small oasis with great order. This is something that I learned in Indonesia, to be very precise. The fields are extremely precise, everything is precise, the dancing, everything is well structured, but it is still an oasis within the larger context of the chaos of the wild nature. Here is another picture of Bali. You can see the structure of the village, the structure of the dressing: everything is structured, organized; but at the same time you know that around there there is also a lot of wild nature.

D I A N A » Do you think the presence of that nature affects their lives?

D O N A » I am sure that the structure of nature affects their lives. You learn through the eyes, you absorb through the eyes. If the man-made nature is organized you tend to reflect that. They also have some interesting tricks. A man owns a herd of ducks and brings them in the morning in the fields. They graze in the rice fields and in the evening he brings them back home. The man has a trick to do that. He does not want to sit in the mud all day long, he wants to go home and do other things. So this is what he does. When the ducks come out of the eggs he puts a bamboo stick in front of them. The first thing they thus see when hatch is the bamboo stick and this becomes 'mamma'. From then on all he has to do in the morning is pick up the bamboo stick, go to the fields and they all go: Quack, quack quack after him. When he gets to the field he puts the bamboo stick in the mud and goes home. The ducklings will hang around there all day long, around their 'mama'. In the evening he goes back, picks up the bamboo stick and heads home. Konrad Lorenz worked with this idea. He put himself in front of duck eggs and when they came out the first thing they saw was this man, this biologist. So he became their 'mamma' to the extent that they were following him everywhere around and he had to do everything for them. He had to teach them how to walk, how to eat, how to swim, and even how to fly, and he documented all this on film. He and his staff running downhill flapping their arms with all the little ducks running after him flapping their wings. Of course they took off eventually and he probably just fell into the lake in the end. He coined this phenomenon the 'imprint vulnerability state'. The first thing that animals see at the moment of birth becomes the nourishing mamma. It does not matter what, as long as it is the first thing they see. It is a natural law.

DIANA » The safety zone.

DONA » It is the first safety zone that human beings and all other animals look for, the nourishing food zone. I use this idea a lot in yoga. When a student comes to the class for the first time he is at the height of his 'yoga imprint vulnerability'. What you give in that moment, the picture that you present in that moment to that person becomes 'mamma', becomes the imprint. After the first imprint the brain closes around that picture and that picture becomes as it were 'hardware'. The same thing happens with language. When a baby is born in America and is ripe for language at the age of two it is like a time bomb, the time bomb for language opens up. At that moment whatever language you put in there the mind, the brain closes over it and that becomes your language. Once it is closed, once that moment is gone, the time bomb is closed, it is very hard to learn a new language. Somebody who is born in America learns American in no time, but when he goes to China when he is twenty years old he has a hard time learning Chinese. On the other hand, a baby born in China, at the age of two, learns Chinese in no time but when he is twenty and has to go to America and learn American it is very hard work because that moment is gone.

DIANA » So in yoga, if you do not have that good example of the visual pose on the first day...

DONA » Exactly. In presenting yoga to somebody the first six months are extremely important, to present as clear, as simple, and as clean a picture as possible. In Eastern countries hypnosis plays an important role, in Bali specially. In the West we have a very black and white view. We have the Devil and we have God. God is the goody and the Devil is the bady. As you know, the goodies have to win like in cowboy movies. The cowboys have to win and the Indians have to lose. This is the traditional good and bad, black and white stuff. In Bali there are two mythical personalities: the Rangda and the Barong. The Rangda is an evil witch with long hair and tongue hanging out of her mouth. She is obviously the bady. The Barong is a mythological lion, he is the goody. But there is one difference and that is that neither of them wins and neither of them loses. It is more like a tango. One time the Rangda is up and the Barong is down, and the other time the Barong is up and the Rangda is down. Like a see-saw it is never so that one is winning forever and the other one losing forever.

TONI » It is more real.

DONA » It is more real in the sense that the good guys and the bad guys both have a chance of winning and losing, or like the yin and the yang symbol where the black and the white form together one circle. If you only have the white or only the black you can never get that nice yin/yang symbol. The people who are doing this dance (the Kris dance in Bali) are put into such a hypnotic state that they take a sword with which they try to pierce themselves. Their minds are so strong with the hypnosis that it makes the skin hard like leather. Even if they work very hard to pierce themselves with the sword the sword does not go in. If, on the other hand, they fall out of their trance the sword will go in and it will kill them. But as long as they are in trance they can try and pierce themselves with the sword and nothing happens. For a while this dance was prohibited because a lot of accidents did happen. It just shows that everything is hypnosis. They also dance on hot coals. They burn a huge pile of coconut shells and the people dance around on the burning coals. It is called the horse dance. The horse-man runs through the coals and does not get burned. Again through hypnosis his foot sole is so thick and impenetrable that he does not get burned. With hypnosis you can do a lot of things. It is the mind that is doing it. We are under a profound hypnosis all the time. When I say that this floor is hard, the floor is not hard at all; it is just empty atoms.

T O N I » We are just falling through it.

D O N A » We are *not* falling through it, that is the whole point. We are just sitting on top of it, which is weird, because we *should* be falling through it, but we are not. This is what I was saying about the puddle and the ripples. The mind should be so smooth that it only reflects what is out there, but if you throw a stone, a memory, or a thought in there it makes the ripples and the clear reflection is broken. This is how we damage the perception of the real universe.

We were talking about the human body. I think that when the human body got upright from the ape state we liberated the hands so we got the big brain, but the spine too was liberated. Therefore I think that acrobatics and movement is inherent in the human body, it is part of the parcel of the human body. That is why I like to do yoga in nature. The body can imitate nature in such a nice way; it can reflect rocks, waves, trees. You can make the body not only stand out in nature, but can also make it blend into nature like the American Indians who used to disappear in the woods. Most people try and stand out but you must be able to do both: standing out and disappearing. That again is that double game, not only one or the other. I often try to make the body disappear in the rock formations, just hint at a posture without getting too much of a gap between the human posture and the rocks.

With animals the size is not important. What is important is the relationship. These horses here are Belgians and those there are called Miniatures horses. It is the same animal but one is seven foot tall and the other comes up to your hip joint. They are different in size but they have the same nature, they live in the same horse-world, their horse-centric world. It is not that the little horse says: "Oh, that is a big horse" and the big horse says: "Oh, that is a little horse." Each one has his own section and each one is perfect in his own way. The little horse is not little; it is a horse. The big horse is not big; it is a horse. In the yoga world we tend to look at bodies and make pseudo - or phantom - judgments: somebody is stiff or supple. But the stiff person is not stiff for himself, he is normal. The supple person is not supple for himself or herself, he or she normal. It is when you look at the other from your own viewpoint that you can make these judgments, comparing. As human beings we have a homo-centric view of the world. I am a human being and everyone else is an animal: this is very arbitrary. Within the homo-centric worldview we also have an ego-centric worldview. I look at the world from my personal perspective and say: "Oh what a cute little hummingbird." Or: "What an aggressive little hummingbird." The hummingbird is not aggressive nor cute nor little. He is just a hummingbird. The hummingbird is doing exactly what in hummingbird world you are supposed to do. He is doing his job, living his life, being perfectly hummingbird-normal. Now, with the same coin the hummingbird may look at me and say: "What a weird, huge, wingless mammal." You see? I'm not a weird, huge, wingless mammal in my eyes. So everything is relative.

40   **Eyes of Innocence**
    Dona Holleman

3   Interview while hiking on Death Canyon Trail

DONA » Water is a very interesting metaphor because it is very clear. It reflects. We were talking yesterday about the puddle and the ripples. Most of the time we look at things like now. We are in these beautiful woods and we are looking at things. This looking is never clear like the water; there are always a lot of things behind the screen, behind the scene. When you look at things you know what you are looking at, there are a lot of memories, there are associations, there are maybe emotions involved in it, and so it is never a clear reflection of what you see.

DIANA » We see ourselves.

DONA » You see through your eyes; it is like a cloud that is in the middle. Instead of reflecting just a straight thing you look through this cloud that is your past. Yesterday we were talking about time. Looking is always done from the perspective of time. Which means that you have the past and that is how you look, from your past experiences. It is never like the water a clear reflection but there are always ripples, clouds. Basically there are two brain functions. There is the 'normal' one, the daily one that we use in order to live in our daily lives. You have to go to the office, you have to do your work, you have to eat, you have to do shopping, so you need your daily mind, which is the homo-centric mind. It is the mind that we use to live in this world. But then you also have the other world. Look at that chipmunk: this is just to show the example of the homo-centric point of view. In the first place you call it a chipmunk, which is a human word because probably he himself does not have a word for himself, or at least a different one from ours. Chipmunk is a human word. Then you have a lot of things to say about it. It is 'cute', it is 'pretty', it is 'fast', it is 'cocky'. These are all human judgments. Or you may say: "What a small animal." In the chipmunk mind, in squirrel life, in the squirrel-centric world, he is not at all small; he is normal. He may think that we are huge, slow. So every species looks at the others from their own species-centric point of view.

DIANA » Should we try to get away from that homo-centric view?

DONA » We have those two functions of the brain. On the one hand we have the function of the brain, which is homo-centric, which places us in the center of the universe. We say: "The stars are out there, the trees are out there, the animals are out there, so I am the center of the universe." But we also have the other mind which some scientist now are calling 'the quantum mind' which is the mind which can temporarily step out of the homo-centric world view and again look at things with non-human eyes, let us say, and thus connect us again with what they would call the quantum web or the quantum world.

DIANA » There is a beautiful cloud.

DONA » Beautiful cloud - everything is beautiful. Again the word 'beautiful' is also a homo-centric word, is it not? A cloud is just a cloud. This is the interesting thing; it is a fascinating subject that all our lives we put words on things. Things are things and then we put words on them and those words have either positive or negative meaning, or a neutral one. But there is always a meaning that we paste onto the thing. The thing is only a thing, a tree is only a tree. It is we who call it beautiful or not beautiful.

DIANA » To pay attention - only pay attention and not put a word in it, would this be the quantum state?

DONA » Yes. The first time I was really in contact with that kind of idea was when I went to India in 1964. I went to a forest. There was a ranger, and he took us around in a jeep. You could not go out of the jeep because of the lions (many people do not know that there are still lions in India, in Ghir Forest Park). He kept on pointing things out: "Do you see the deer there, do you see the bird there, do you see the animal there?" I did not see a thing and I thought to myself: "What is wrong with me?" Then I realized that these people have learned to pay attention. Their eyes are so fast, they knew exactly how to look. Afterwards I began to train myself. I thought: "This is ridiculous that I cannot see." So now I train my eyes. Then I realized something else about paying attention. When you look back at the moment of attention you realize that you did not think in that moment of paying attention. I realized that thinking and attention cannot occupy the same space at the same time. I think that that is what they mean with the quantum mind and the continuous mind. The continuous mind, the thinking mind is the mind that moves in time and that includes thinking, it includes planning. Thinking has to do with words, with sentences and with pictures.

It is the inner world. Plato had the cave idea: in the cave analogue the people were watching the images on the inside of the cave. This is what we do all the day long. The skull is the cave and we watch the images on the inner walls of the cave. Those images are bound to language. The art of attention is very different. Attention is not a linear line from the past through the present to the future but rather like a series of dots. You can only be attentive for a millionth of a second and then again you have to be attentive and again attentive and again attentive. It is not a continuous thing. It is an act, which is outside the space/time boundaries. That is the quantum mind, which is not contained in time and space. It is outside time and space. As human beings we have both possibilities. That is where the tightrope image comes in. Usually we live entirely in the continuous mind, in our man-made world, the world where there are memories, associations and words. It is the cave with the images on the inside. But the 'real' things are outside.

DIANA » What happens when you get that dot, that experience, that moment. What happens when you come back? What is different then?

DONA » Well, the interesting thing is that when you pay full attention and you are outside the time sequencing you do not have a memory afterwards, because in order to have a memory you need to construct it.

DIANA » Like a dream?

DONA » No, not like a dream. It is an awareness, which does not leave a residue. There is a difference between 'looking' and 'seeing'. I think that some writers have made the same kind of division. 'Looking' is to look at things, to recognize things, like you recognize the trees, the animals, and in the recognition you 'damage' what you see. It is the puddle and the ripples again. Instead of having the clear reflection, when the ripples come it distorts the reflection. That is the damaging part of it, that is the 'harming'. It is necessary and useful to 'look' because I have to know that that is a tree and I cannot walk through it, but the flip side of it is that the cloud, the image, the memory, comes in the middle and I cannot really come close to the tree. I cannot come close because there is something in the middle and what is in the middle is 'me'. 'Seeing' is when the 'me' is out of the way so that I can come very close into the tree and the tree and I can have a real quantum exchange which is not an emotional thing.

DIANA » What is that quantum exchange?

DONA » Looking at things with the continuous mind, memory has to do with the brain. It has to do with intellectual processing and with emotions. When I 'look' I can be emotional about something. If I 'look' at the squirrel I can say: "Oh, cute little squirrel" and I get all mushy about it. That is a false relationship. It is a false relationship because the squirrel is not 'cute' and 'small'; the squirrel is simply a squirrel. It is my words of 'cute' and 'small' that get in the way and makes the whole thing mushy and emotional. That is 'looking'. Instead, if I'm 'seeing' things, in the act of 'seeing', because I do not put anything on what I am seeing, there is no emotional contact but there is another contact that is not emotional. It is no 'cute little thing' and 'beautiful little tree' and 'wonderful cloud'. Because there are no words attached to it there is a different contact, a contact that has to do with the body and with something in the heart, in the heart of the body. I do a lot of reading about quantum physics. These scientists are taking us by the hand and leading us into some incredible horizons.

DONA » We can intuitively feel a lot of things but these scientists give body to what we feel. One of the things that the scientists are working on is that when two particles meet and bump into each other as it were they share afterwards the same information; they fuse the information into one thing. As, since the beginning of the Big Bang, the beginning of creation, all the particles have bumped into each other the whole of the universe shares the same 'information'. This is one of the biggest things that blew my brain -

that the whole of the universe shares the same information and that includes our bodies because our bodies are also made of particles and atoms. Therefore I always say that each human being is complete. We have it all. We have all the information we need, we have all the tools we need to go out there and have a one-to-one relationship with the universe because we are a completely integral part of it. We are not separate and out of the earth, out of the universe; we are an integral part of it. Thus all we need to do is to acknowledge this, to understand that yes, we made this nice little oasis in this huge sea of the universe but we are still part of it all. By the way, I heard that the name Maria comes from Miriam, which means 'bitter ocean or bitter sea'.

DIANA » I know: 'mar' 'yam'. Mar-yam, yes.

DONA » So like a bitter sea, this huge ocean, this huge sea that we are swimming in is the universe. And human beings and all the animals, each one makes their own little oasis in this sea, their own little island. This is done with the continuous mind but we also have the other side, we also have the body that shares the same information of all of the universe, so when you look at a tree you can look it at it either from a perspective of the human being and say: "What a beautiful tree, what a nice tree, what an ugly tree," or you can switch to the other side and use your body and your heart to look at the tree and then it is a question of the atoms looking at the tree, the universe looking at itself, aware of itself, loving itself. This is what the scientists say: that the universe is self aware, because information is the same everywhere, it is just a question of being aware of the tree from the same level, from an atomic level, let us say.

DIANA » So it is a matter in a way of putting the brain, the thoughts and the past on the side, to 'collapse' them.

DONA » Yes, and this is another thing which I find really interesting. Einstein found out that time and space were, as it were, fused together, were one thing, that we live in a four dimensional world, and moreover that time is flexible, space is flexible. This is what I was saying yesterday. Sometimes one minute lasts a century and sometimes one year flies by in 'no time'.

DIANA » That is the psychological time?

DONA » That is the psychological time that we always live in. The awareness of the quantum world is outside this structure of time and space, of psychological time, and so there is a different touch and therefore you cannot say what kind of touch that is because you cannot put it into language, because language is four-dimensional.

JOSH » They say that there are more than four dimensions, that we are within a four-dimensional membrane within a mega-verse that contains something like thirteen dimensions which we cannot even conceive of.

DONA » Yeah, some say eleven, some say ten, some say fourteen. I am not sure that they still know what it is but it is a lot of dimensions.

JOSH » Absolutely.

DONA » That is the fun part of it because the continuous mind, the brain, the electric unit that we have inside can only deal with four dimensions but the body - being of the same material as everything else - can deal with those eleven dimensions. It is a bodily feeling of being in touch with everything else which is very different from the intellectual feeling. This is where we come back to ideas and philosophies. You can never love a philosophy, you cannot touch it, you cannot see it, you cannot feel it, smell it. It is an intellectual love, but never a bodily love. But a tree, you can touch it and there is a vibration going back and forth, there is a feeling going back and forth which you cannot describe, which you cannot put into words. It is a feeling between the thing and you. You can touch it, you can smell it, you can hear it. It is a bodily thing, a bodily contact. I think that we cling to the intellectual world because we do not know how to do it, to have this atomic contact, and so we make theories on how to do it but the theory gets in the way between me and the doing of it.

J O S H » But don't you think it is also just this constant effort to describe that? Like you are speaking about physics, which is obviously an attempt to describe these things that are beyond our ability to even comprehend. We were speaking about the chipmunk earlier and that sort of thing, well just like the chipmunk does not bother to think about whether or not it is going to look for nuts or whatever it is that a chipmunk does, I think that we were born with this instinct to want to describe that part that you are talking about, the non-intellectual side of us.

D O N A » I do think that animals plan like us, but we call it dumbly 'instinct'. I think that the word 'instinct' is a human attempt to say that we do not know about the animals. I do not think that an animal would call it instinct. I think that there is definitely also an intellectual capacity in animals to reason things out but not the way we do. We have this brain because we do not have anything else to protect us in this world. We had to get on, we had to survive in one way or another and the brain - being pretty smart - can outsmart all the animals. Thanks to the brain you can make a boat that goes faster than the shark and you can make an airplane that goes faster than the eagle, so we can outsmart the animals by the electric brain that we have been given. But it is also a very young brain. It is kind of putting a Ferrari motor on a double deck bus. The body is like a double deck bus and the brain is like a Ferrari motor and so it tends to run away with itself and to think that whatever it constructs that is the final thing, that is the real universe, the real life, which of course it is not.

D I A N A » If somebody comes up and tells me: "I am happy with my brain, with my perception, with those ripples, I am happy with looking at the world with my past, and all that. Why do all this, why go beyond that?"

D O N A » It is like yoga, like everything else. Not everybody wants to do it. But the feeling of alienation is there and people are not aware of it. They are only aware of it in a subliminal level. I think that a lot of the time we know that we have lost some contact, that we have taken ourselves out of the universe, out of nature and out of the world and most of the time we are happy with that but at the same time we are also unhappy because we assume too big a role in a universe which actually is so much bigger and faster than we can even imagine.

Sometimes I go out at night to look at the stars, at the constellations. Between the constellation of Cassiopeia and Pegasus is the constellation of Andromeda and if you have very strong binoculars you can see the Andromeda Nebula, a tiny smudge in the sky. That nebula is a universe in itself, a different universe from ours, and it is one and a half million light years away from us. Now, light travels at the speed of 186,000 miles a second so if you multiply the seconds to make a minute and then from a minute to an hour and from an hour to a day and from a day to a year and then multiply by 1½ million - I think you get a pretty good idea of how big the universe is. Thus, to place ourselves in the middle of this and say that we know it all and we are the crown of all this is, to say the least, ridiculous. It brings you back to a more realistic perspective.

We have been given this brain and it is useful, but it can also get in the way. Many people are happy the way they are. But at the same time they are not and I think that that is why we have invented so many religions, so many philosophies, gurus. You look around and you see so many gurus. People are desperately looking for something or somebody to tell them how to live. We never have that one-to-one relationship with life that we talked about yesterday. We always go somewhere else, we ask the other person to describe life to us, to tell us how to live. Our perception always loops through the church, the temple, someone else, something else. Thus we always get a glimpse of the universe second hand, through the other person, through the system. As I was saying before, each one of us is complete in the same way that the chipmunk is complete. The chipmunk is complete, he is completely there and we are all complete. We can have that one-to-one relationship if we switch between the two brains.

J O S H » Do you put a value judgment on each brain?

D O N A » No value judgments. Value judgments belong to the continuous brain.

J O S H » Right, but it sounds like the continuous brain is the one that is constantly fooling us.

D O N A » It is fooling us but as I say, it is also necessary to be 'fooled'. The interesting thing is that most of the time people do not know that we create the world and that we are then trapped in the world and ruled by it. That world, as it traps us, pressurizes on us. That is what we feel as suffering. We have to live with the continuous mind but, at the same time, we have to be aware that we do it ourselves, that it is a man-made world. Once you are really aware that you are living in a man-made world you are already outside of it, you are not pressurized by it. You can look at it with humor, you can laugh at it because you are not pressed by it.

D I A N A » So emotional problems - to deal with the emotions, it maybe not even worth while going into them. Just knowing that they are part of...

D O N A » Emotions belong to the man-made world and to the continuous mind; they do not belong to the universe itself. They are typically human. They are a human reaction to something. An emotion is never an action in itself; you cannot initiate an emotion. An emotion is always the ball bouncing back towards something else. You have a thought or somebody comes and you have a bad memory about that person. The emotion is always a reaction to something from the outside or from the inside. You cannot initiate just out of the blue an emotion.

A N E T T E » So it is from the outside or the inside?

D O N A » Either. It can be a thought, it can be a memory or it can be something from the outside. And the emotion and the thought are reactions to that. While the other touch - what we were talking of before - touching nature around us in that different way is not emotional. There is no emotion involved in it.

D O N A » That is what they say when you go Scuba diving. You should only take pictures, you should only bring yourself.

J O S H » Told you guys how I crossed the ocean ... the saddest thing about crossing the ocean is how many times you pass bits of plastic floating in the ocean. Think about how many there must be if you are in the middle of the ocean and you cross like a six-pack ring floating by or like a milk jug or something like that. It means there have to be so many of them because they are so small and a boat is such a small thing and the ocean is so big.

D O N A » That is again the homo-centric point of view that we think that everything belongs to us and so we can throw everything away in nature because nature belongs to us, the ocean belongs to us, we do not care what we do because we are the top of the top and we can do what we want with it. It is again that very limited view.

D I A N A » I am interested in what you were saying about our having this atomic interchange with nature and how we do not need a guru or anyone to explain to us nature as we can do it ourselves... we have the same atoms.

D O N A » In the Middle Ages people had the view - scientists and non-scientists alike - that there was something called the ether. The whole universe was filled with this ether. In India they had the same idea. They called it the 'akasha'. Everything was the akasha, the ether, and everything was sitting - swimming - in the ether including the earth and the sun and people and trees; everything was contained in the ether. Then when science got a little bit more sophisticated they said: "No, this idea of the ether is medieval, let us forget about it." Then they discovered that there was something that they called the electro-dynamic field or the quantum field. Now they are moving again into new definitions. They are inching their way back into the idea of the ether and the fact that there is no empty space. Diana, you think that there is empty space between the two of us but in reality there is not because there is nitrogen, there is oxygen, there are vibrations, and also you and I are shedding all the time dead cells from the skin and electricity and all this is flying in all directions. You and I are breathing all the time so we share the air. You and I are emitting electricity, which is why today everyone in the house got shocks from the carpet and from each other, electrical shocks, because the air is so dry; you get the static electricity. If you have a blouse that is polyester, artificial material, and you take it off, specially when you take it off at night, you see the lights and you get electrical shocks. So there is a lot of exchange going on and there is no way - absolutely no way - in all this to know where you end and I begin or where I end and you begin. It is like Indian raw silk, a smooth surface with bubbles, warps, in it. The universe is like that, smooth silk, and each one of us is a warp in the silk, or a hologram. Or when they say that there is an electro-dynamic field, you can also compare this to a jelly. Everything is a jelly and we are holograms in the jelly. There are so many ways that you can think of the whole thing, but basically there is only one thing and everything that exists, the squirrels and us and the camera and everything else is just a hologram or an imperfection in the perfect jelly. This is a nice image and makes you really feel that we are not in empty space, that between me and the tree there is not empty space. My body can touch it, my body can feel it; even at a distance my body can feel it and of course I can lean against it and that is even better as an exchange between the tree and me. We are - both of us - imperfections in the perfect void-which-is-not-void.

DIANA » Why is it so hard for us to realize that we can do it all ourselves, that we are perfect and not need anyone or anything.

DONA » I do not know. Maybe it is some kind of a residue from prehistoric times when people were alone in woods like these and there were not only just squirrels but there were also tigers and lions and all kinds of scary things: lightning and thunder and people did not have the intellectual know-how; they were bombarded by scary things and wanted an explanation, they wanted to know how to deal with it all. They wanted somebody to take care of them and this is how they then appointed a special person to do that for them. Those were the shamans. The shaman was the man - or woman - who could explain it all to them and who could interfere, keep the thunder away or bring the rain in or call the buffalo when they were hungry or take the bear away. He could interfere for the people because of the fear of the people themselves. This is still a residue that we continue to look for the expert to give us clues of what to do. But that time of the scary things of prehistory is over and yet there is nobody - or there are very few people - who tell us clearly that we can do it ourselves, that we can deal with the universe ourselves. It is not in the interest of the gurus and the priests to tell us that we can do it ourselves.

DANIEL» That is also related to the same idea of the religions, to explain all of those things that scared us and we had no explanation for.

DONA» Yeah, the major religions, the ones that we know like Buddhism, Hinduism, Islam, Judaism, Christianity are late religions. They are only 2,000-3,000 years old. But before that people's religious idea was of the creative force often expressed in the Earth Mother, the Great Goddess, because it was such an abundant life: all the animals being born and dying and people born and dying in endless cycles. That old religion was very nature oriented but the religions that are now are in a way an attempt to take us away from nature and natural contact, and instead intellectualize God and the universe.

DIANA» You think that maybe the sophistication in those religions actually took us away from the real religion?

DONA» I think evolution goes in spirals. In the old days people were more in close contact with nature and with the natural forces, with the creative force, because the creative force is in here, you can feel it pulsating. This creative force, people were in contact with it, but they did not have the intellectual capacity, so we had to make a circle to come to an intellectual state in our development, in our evolution. But now, I think scientists are spiraling back to the fact that we are an integral part of nature and therefore we can have that quantum contact.

DIANA » Why did you say that it was not in man's best interest to tell man that he can do it on his own?

DONA » There is a lot of business involved in the big religions, philosophies and sects. The business is an important part of it. If you tell people to just go home and do it themselves you lose the business. I think that this is happening anyway. In the grassroots society people are realizing that they can go out in the woods and again reestablish their own personal link with the universe, as each human being has that link. It is like a shining thread. But we are either unaware - ignorant - about it or we are a bit nervous about it: low self-esteem. So we say: "That man has a nice big thread going to the universe, let us hook into that."

DIANA » Better connection.

DONA » Better connection.

DIANA » Fast Internet connection.

DONA » Yeah, fast Internet connection. But as each human being is complete and has his own link you can take care of your own link, take responsibility. We need to take responsibility for being here, to take care of our own personal link, to smooth it and make it shining, strong and resilient. It can be done; each one can take care of our own link to the universe and make that strong and resilient. That is our responsibility.

DIANA » What can you tell us about how that has affected your personal life?

DONA » That is what I do. All the time I think: "It is my responsibility." There is nobody like me, I am the only one in the world, like you are the only one in the world, Anette is the only one in the world. Chris is the only one in the world; there is nobody like Chris.

CHRIS » Thank you.

DONA » Each one of us has a special, a particular link to the universe and nobody else can duplicate that, no priest, no church, no sect can duplicate that link to the universe. Then we come back to the animals. What I was saying the other day is that animals are proud. Now the big religions, the sects, the gurus tell us to be humble. This is really terrible because that humility is a false humility. It is a humility concocted by the ego. Now you see a little chipmunk, a little bird, a bird that size singing on a branch: he owns the whole world and he knows it and he is singing away there. Somehow, if that bird would not be there there would be a hole on that branch, something would be missing. In the same way if we would not be standing here there would be a hole in this area. Animals fill up that hole very nicely.

DIANA » So a squirrel is not humble?

DONA » Not at all humble. He is just being a squirrel. He is all excited about being a squirrel; he is doing his thing. He is filling up the squirrel hole where he is and he is filling it up to the brim. Human beings are the only ones that are taught in school and from school onward that you have to be meek, you have to be humble, you have to shrink within the hole that you are occupying.

ANETTE » I know exactly what you mean.

DONA » It is awful because they tell me to be humble, to become humble. That means that they are telling me to get rid of the ego, only then are you OK. Not realizing that getting rid of the ego is a time process, it is a spatial process, and thus it belongs to the ego. You tell the ego to get rid of itself. It is not going to do that, so the humility that you get is a phantom humility, a show.

JOSH » It is more shame than humility.

DIANA » It is arrogance.

DONA » It is the flip side of arrogance. You put on special clothes or a special sign, wearing special things to show that you are humble, that you are spiritual. It is the flip side of arrogance because you want to stand out as being humble. It is very interesting; you have to be very careful. The only real moment of humility is when there is no ego which is in that moment of attention: when we are paying full attention to a tree, or to the sky, in that moment there is no time, there is no space, and therefore there is no ego. That is the moment of humility.

CHAPELA» Can it be done all the time?

D O N A » It cannot be 'done', that is the whole point, you cannot tell the ego to be humble. It requires a quantum leap. People tell me that I have to do meditation, I have to do this for a long time and then I will come to a point that is timeless. It cannot be done. The quantum leap means that you 'disappear' out of the continuous mind, which includes the ego and everything else, and 'appear' in the quantum mind. But you cannot 'go' from here to there. Anything you do to go from here to there is an act of the ego.

J O S H » Is it something that can be shared? Maybe the act of sharing means that you are 'doing' something so you are not in the moment but, as you were talking about having a one-to-one connection with a tree, is it something that human beings can have with each other as well?

D O N A » Of course, but not in the context of helping the other person.

J O S H » Just experiencing them.

D O N A » We do that all the time anyway, we share all the time anyway, even on a subliminal level, unless you train yourself to become aware of these things. Sometimes you go near a certain person and you think "I want to get closer", because there is a certain attraction, you do not know why or how. Or somebody else comes and you want to back away from that person because there is some wave coming at you which you find repelling. There is always that sharing going on between the two. But the real sharing is of course when both simultaneously can be in that quantum state.

DIANA » I also think that it relates to what you were saying that the only real teaching is by being an example, in a sense the visual teaching.

D O N A » You cannot help another, you cannot teach another; you cannot be an example either because if you are an example, then again it is something that you are doing. A sunflower is a sunflower and going near the sunflower makes you joyous, not because the sunflower wants to be an example for you. The sunflower is just a sunflower. But being there makes you feel happy because it is a happy flower.

DIANA » Does nature help to get a more direct experience of the world? Coming out to the woods helps to get that direct experience?

DONA » I think so, yes. Because the life force is here, the creative force; everything is alive in nature. Stones are alive, wood is alive, the trees, the clouds and the animals, everything is alive, pulsating. Our bodies are also alive so I think that it is much easier to pick up that contact, to get that link with the universal force.

DIANA » And also being close to animals.

DONA » Close to animals; we can learn from animals that 360-degree vision all around. We can learn from the animals, we can see how they deal with their world, how it can help us in our own lives. Since I teach yoga, I learn most from the animals, because each animal has a particular way of moving and those movements are often very harmonious and beautiful. My body feels them. You see an eagle flying and your body feels the power of the wings or you see a cat moving, a puma moving, you feel the smoothness of the movement and then your body likes to copy because bodies like to copy. Bodies are copy machines.

DIANA » The visual image.

DONA » The visual image. The body likes that, because the body is also an animal, the body is part of all this, it is part of nature, and so the body picks up that grace from nature, that energy from nature, and can use it. While the mind has a different circuit which is more an internal circuit. It has an electrical contact with nature but not through the cells, nor through direct contact as we were saying just now.

DIANA » So while doing an asana you might think of that movement of the animal and project that movement?

D O N A » Well, more than think of the specific movement, think of the energy that makes that movement, the particular intent of that movement. Which the yogis did in the old days; many postures that we do are called after animals so probably they observed the animals and gave the posture their name. Also if you see so-called primitive tribes they are always dancing. Dancing is part of the life of human beings; whether it is yoga postures, or dancing, the body wants to move and it wants to move in the larger context of nature, copying animals, copying nature. The American Indians, the Africans always dancing outside, directly there. Not like our ballet where you go to the theater.

D I A N A » And that dancing is that moment of total attention? Can it be that moment of total attention?

D O N A » I think that dancing was one of the things that people did straight away after becoming people. Homo erectus began to dance straight away; it is in-built in the human body. I think it is a two way street: the human being dances to go into a trance, like in Bali, and also the American Indians. We saw just now the buffalo dances in New Mexico. Those dancers go on for hours and hours in the hot sun and I am sure that they induce some kind of a trance situation where the intellectual brain kind looses its barriers, its grip, and so another type of contact sets in. But I also think it can be the other way around, that people get into a quantum state and then out of the quantum state dance, for instance the Quakers. They are called 'Quakers', because when they went into prayer and got into direct contact with the force, they began to shake. That is why there were called Shakers or Quakers because their bodies began to shake, to quake, when they went into a deep internal state.

J O S H » Another example is that babies dance before they know how to speak language, before they know how to walk even. If you play music for a baby, it will dance.

D O N A » You see it also with grown ups. The brain of the grown up has a very strong grip on the body and the emotions; it is imprisoned, but when you are on a holiday, going to the beach, you get completely silly. You run around and play with the ball and do all kinds of things because the intellectual grip is loosened up a little bit in holiday state and so, suddenly, the body begins to run, and jump, and splash in the water and play with the ball. Because the human body just loves to do that. It is the expression of the joy of being alive. It is the force that runs through the atoms of the body and makes it move.

DIANA » So that is another state: 'the holiday state'?

DONA » The holiday state.

ANETTE» I love that one.

DONA » The quantum state is the holiday state, getting out of this eternal grip of the serious brain state.

ANETTE» Do you think that practicing yoga as a way to free the body will help us to be more in a kind of vacation state all the time?

DONA » No.

ANETTE» Not at all?

DONA » We come back to the same thing we have been talking about before. Everything you do, whatever you do, is going to trip you up. If you use yoga in order to get into the holiday state, into the quantum state, it is going to trip you up because it is still within time and space. Whatever you do it can bring you in to some kind of a phantom holiday state but it is not the real thing. It is the quantum leap. You have to stop doing everything in order to be in the other state. Yoga is very nice because it is a complete package for the body. It is more complete than any other sport or activity for the body, if you really practice yoga with the breathing, doing all of the postures. Then that makes the atoms of the body loose. That is the only thing it can do. Yoga makes the atoms of the body loose and so the body is more receptive. But you cannot invite the other; you cannot invite the force to come in. You can only be receptive and then it may or may not come; the contact flirt, the quantum flirt, may come or not come. But you cannot say: "I want it." You cannot 'work' for it, you cannot do anything to 'get' it because whatever you do is going to trip you up.

DIANA » What about the city, living in concrete. What can happen there in this matter of direct experience being far away from nature.

DONA » The ether is everywhere, the quantum field is everywhere. Stones, bricks, cement, everything is pulsating with life. Probably everything is pulsating with conscious life even; but in the city there is also a lot of electric interference from other people so it is maybe not so easy to get that link smooth without static interference from outer thoughts and people. In that way it is easier in nature because everything is quieter, more in harmony with each other. Not so many thoughts going around in nature. But life is pulsating everywhere, in the city, in nature, everywhere.

CHRIS » You would not consider a city as divorced from nature. Would you consider a city as part of nature too?

DONA » A city is definitely part of life, it is part of everything. There you go back again into this thing, that we always divide, divide. The divisions that we make are arbitrary and man made. You say 'nature' is 'beautiful' and 'the city' is 'ugly'. This is an arbitrary and man-made division. We were saying about the mouse the other day. A mouse can go in the city or it can go into the field, and I do not think it says: "The city is ugly and the field is beautiful." This is a man-made arbitrary thing and has to do with our likes and dislikes, with our preferences, with the past. I have known people who go into nature, they see a tree and they run for their life back into the cement concrete because they get scared, they think it is terrible to be among the trees. I have known people like that. So, it is arbitrary: some people like this, some people like that, but life is everywhere. It is not that in the city there is no life; there is life everywhere.

DIANA » Maybe when we live in the city and are surrounded only by man-made things we forget our place in the universe and when we go out here in nature the perspective comes back as a shock?

DONA » The perspective comes back as a shock because in the city the temptation to do a lot of things is much bigger. You know, you have so many distractions in the city; it is not a question that the force is not there. The force is everywhere, life is everywhere, but in the city you are more distracted, you have more things to do. You have to go to the job, you have to earn money to live, so it is much easier to take a little bit of distance every now and then and go into nature to re-connect yourself and then see if you can keep the connection in the city also. There is less distraction in nature, that is all. But life is everywhere, also in the city. The city is steaming with life. There is something which I did not know and which I find very interesting. In our galaxy there are billions and billions of stars, and then there is this tiny planet. On this tiny planet there are, I think, about one million two hundred thousand species of living animals. Out of that one million two hundred thousand species about one million is beetles. Then there is two hundred thousand species of other animals: insects and other animals. As human beings we are at the bottom of the line, we are not even the width of a hair on the circle of life on earth. We are so few of us. So if you zoom in on city life it has all these insects, beetles, many more than people. Therefore you cannot say that life is not in the city. You may not like the beetles but that again is a human, arbitrary, and homo-centric view of beetles. Who knows, the beetle may not like us either. That would be the beetle-centric point of view.

DIANA » I wonder why so many people are looking for gurus. There is this need, this emotional need, because of unhappiness, a lack of something.

DONA » It is not having the trust in the link.

ANETTE» Yes.

DIANA » You think that not having the trust in the link is a human problem. Our own private personal problems are the same for everyone. We just have to realize that that is the problem, so it is the same solution for everyone. It is not like a particular emotional problem for each person. I think this can really help us get out of that small space we confine ourselves in; we think our problems are so big. Maybe our problems are the same as the other person's problems and we should not even get into the particulars.

D O N A » I think that that is definitely the case. I think that this is a purely human thing, a global human thing, that kind of desperation. There is the feeling of alienation because we have taken ourselves out of nature. Even in our own psychological make-up we talk about people and animals, people and nature. We are talking about us 'being' in nature as if we are not 'nature in nature'. We are nature in nature. This feeling of alienation which creates that feeling that we are outside, that we do not belong, that we are lacking something, that we need somebody else to guide us, we need somebody to help us. This is part of the reason why there are so many problems specially in a city where there are a lot of people. Human problems, human desperation problems; it is the same for everybody.

J O S H » I think that relates to what you were saying earlier about our brains. As far as our bodies are concerned we are not as well equipped as the animals are, we do not have big teeth, big claws, but our intellect allows us to be faster than the animals, stronger than the animals. That part that comes along with that intellect is maybe born with the feeling that everything else is better equipped than you are and that you are not part of nature; that you need to figure out a way to triumph over it.

D O N A » That we are above it.

J O S H » Yeah, that we need to triumph over it.

D O N A » The brain is in that sense a double edge sword. On the one hand we need it, we need the brain and we need the ego, we need the continuous mind because that is the way we are. We have been created with this brain, we cannot throw it out and say: "Oh, I do not want this thing." Whatever is here has been given and we cannot throw it out. It is part of us: the ego is part of us, the brain is part of us, but it is the vortex again. We get drawn in there and we do not know that we can get out. But we can get out. We can take a little distance and use the brain, use the ego as a tool. That is all. Just use it as a tool in the same way as you use your body as a tool, but we get sucked into it and then that fills the whole horizon, it fills the whole dome of the sky instead of being just one of the many tools that we have. The ego is a tool; we need to live with it. You need to have the brain, ego and all those things but they are only tools, they are not the whole thing.

J O S H » It is interesting that you said tool because we are the only animals that need tools to survive.

Eyes of Innocence
       Dona Holleman

4   **Interview indoors at Clymer House**

DONA » In the 1920 movies when there was no sound or speaking the actors had to do everything with their bodies. They are really wonderful to watch because, if you really look carefully at their bodies and movements, you can see a lot of things that we have lost. I look and when I see them, I use them. I say: "What can I do with it and how can I integrate it into my own yoga practice and into the teaching of yoga." I see this movement of Douglas Fairbanks, which comes up from the ankles through the legs into the hip joints, and then the whole body lifts up from the hip joints. This is a movement that I have never seen before, maybe only few people ever show this kind of movement. Most people sag in their hip joints and in their joints in general, there is no upward drive in the body. This actor (Douglas Fairbanks) was asked by a journalist how this movement got into his body and he (Douglas Fairbanks) seemed to think it was due to a combination of boxing and gymnastics. He did a lot of boxing and these were his passions: gym and boxing. He seemed to think that he got that lightness and the activity of the ankles due to boxing. You can see very clearly in this scene here (the movie 'Zorro') how his whole body is driven upwards through the ankles, the legs, and the hip joints into the rest of the body. How he gets that height which is extremely lovely if you know what you look for. It is a lovely movement.

The other thing he was famous for and which I enjoy tremendously is the quicksilverness of his movements, the speed of his movements. You can see this fast movement, the quicksilverness of the movement when he runs and jumps which is in contrast to other bodies. There is something that pulls him. There is some kind of force that pulls his body forward. People were baffled by his movements; they did not know how he did it. He said that he had studied yoga and in the 1920's - I am not sure what kind of yoga there was around - but I think it was mainly Yogananda in Santa Monica. Yogananda had just set up his Ashram there; but also there was a lot of traffic with India and China. I think that Fairbanks did a lot of traveling in India and China and he must have learned some martial arts in China and some yoga in India. He said that he had learned about the use of a certain energy, which he could combine with his physical energy, with his muscle energy and that gave him that tremendous speed and lightness which made him different from everybody else. It was a mental thing that he had learned through yoga and probably through some martial arts, Chinese martial arts. The 'chi' energy, or whatever energy, which he could actually manipulate and use and paste onto his physical energy. If your eyes are trained and if you really look for it you can see it in his fast motions. His body is just flying. His body is flying because there is nothing to hold him back. He is being pulled and he does not 'bump' into or against the air. When you see most people moving it is a heavy pushing forward of the body. The body is kind of wading through the air pushing forward through the air and the air is like a thick jelly through which they push. With him the jelly disappears and when he goes he goes just pffiuuhh! as if there is no jelly whatsoever in front of him, so he is very fast. He is fast forward; he is also fast upward. He can jump up very fast, his speed is just incredible, the speed and the lightness. That is definitely due to this different type of energy that he studied and learned about.

DIANA » He projected the 'energy body'.

DONA » He did not call it the 'energy body'. He called it a 'different type of energy'. He did not go too much into it, because he kind of lost the journalist who asked him about it. He tried to explain it to the journalist, but he lost him somewhere in the explanation. I am sure that it was his 'energy body'. He said that he had learned to empty his mind and then project his mind outside his body. In that way he could use that energy and then project the movement that he was going to do. This I learned from him: the power of visualization. What he said was that every jump he did, every fast forward movement he did, he visualized beforehand. He practiced and practiced, sometimes for weeks, for just one sequence in the movie that lasts two, three seconds. Then after practicing and practicing, when he did the movement, he visualized it beforehand. I think that between the visualization and this extra energy that he had he let his body be pulled through the movements.

DIANA » Is it important to empty the mind beforehand?

DONA » Definitely. You can actually see that before he does his jump or his run he pauses for one, two, three seconds like a cat. Like a cat when he is looking at a mouse, wanting to jump on it, or the lion wanting to jump on the antelope. All the energy is pulled inward, tied together, prepared, and then... pffuif! it is let loose. Once it is let loose there is nothing to stop it. If the energy is on the outside then it is all over the place, scattered. In the visualization you pull everything inward first, you make it very small and tight, like a spring, you pull the spring in. When you have done your visualization and you are ready then you let go of the spring so that the movement is very fast.

DIANA » Do you want to talk about the hips and the ankles?

DONA » The human body has the center of gravity in the pelvis, halfway between the navel and the pubic bone, right in front of the second sacral vertebrae. This is the measurement of the human body. This is the point from which the body is upheld in a healthy body. Now some people will keep the body up from the chest. When you have a proud chest and keep the body up from there then the lower part of the trunk and legs are kind of hanging from your chest. Other people keep the body up from the pelvis but the chest kind of sinks into the pelvis. What I saw in Fairbanks is something I had never seen before. He puts his center of gravity right in the ankle region between the ankles and the insertion of the calf muscle, like a goat. Goat ankles, I call him goat-ankles, because the whole body is driven upwards from the ankles through the legs into the hip joints. You can see that he is still, pulling all the energy inward, and then he suddenly pulls the whole body up and runs. It is the initiation of a very fast movement. I have never seen those movements anywhere and I am thrilled to see them because my passion is the body and how the body moves. Bodies are so unnatural in general, so slow and cumbersome, pushing against space, pushing against the air. With men like these the body just flies through the air, which is very interesting, very sweet to see.

DIANA » Does this lift have to do with the mula bandha?

DONA » Yeah, it definitely has to do with the mula bandha. Based on what I saw I went into breaking the body down into bandhas because I saw this movement and I thought this is really interesting because the body is together. It is one unit, but at the same time there is a sequential force running through it. Seeing the action of the ankles I zoomed in - as it were - on his feet and I worked on how the foot initiates the action. This I have called pada bandha. Then from the feet, from the legs, the thrust goes into the lower abdomen, into that central point of the gravity and then from there it explodes throughout the whole body. So definitely it has to do with the mula bandha. I will show that also in the Mula bandha breathing.

DIANA » What are the Bandhas?

DONA » The word 'bandha' in Sanskrit means 'to bind' like binding, bound. These are places in the body where energy can be bound and contained. A container is never a flat surface but is always round, so round containers in the body are its arches. The body is full of arches because the human body has to stand upright. On the one hand gravity is pulling the body downward, and this is a strong force even though we are not aware of it. On the other hand there is the whole sky sitting on top of the head. I forget how much, but the air has a lot of weight per square inch on the skin of the body. There is an enormous amount of weight. It is like when you go into the deep sea. The more you go down the more weight of the water is on top of you. So when you come up again you have to be very careful. It is the same with the air. The air weighs down on us so the human body has all that weight crushing it down plus the gravity pulling it down. Thus it is an enormous job to keep the body up. Nature has created many arches in the body - the arch in the foot, the arch in the pelvis, the arch in the diaphragm, the arch in the throat, in the jaw. These arches function to keep the weight of the body up, but they can also collect energy. They have a double function. They can bear a lot of weight plus they can contain energy. Where we find the major arches in the body there are the bandhas. They are meant to uphold the body against the downward push and pull and to collect the upward driving force from the ground. This is because gravity does not only pull us down with a certain force, but inherent in gravity there is a counter force which pushes us back up again, otherwise we could not stand. This counter force - which I call the rebounding force - pushes us back up again. So, on the one hand, the arches have the function of keeping at bay the weight. On the other hand to catch from underneath the rebounding force and push the body up.

DIANA » You invented the pada bandha. The other bandhas come from the yoga texts?

DONA » In the classical texts you find a description of three bandhas. These are classical Indian texts dealing with yoga. As I said, however, I would like to take yoga out of the locality of the India of 2000 years ago because we here and now still have the same body. So we have to bring yoga into our time, our culture. In the classical Indian texts about yoga you find the mention of mula bandha, which is the pelvic diaphragm, uddhyana bandha, which is the lower thoracic diaphragm, and jalandhara bandha, which has to do with the upper thoracic diaphragm, the upper ring of the chest. Those were the three classical bandhas, which are situated in the trunk of the body. These texts did not talk about the hands and feet, probably because for them they were obvious. But if you see paintings or sculptures of, for instance, the Buddha, then you always find on the hands and on the soles of the feet painted wheels, circles. That is exactly what a bandha is, a circle, a wheel, a container for energy. They did know about the palms of the hands and the soles of the feet but they never mentioned them in the yoga texts, which is illogical, because we do not only have a trunk. We also have legs and arms and so we have to include them in the totality of the body. That is what I try to do so I added the bandhas in the hand and the bandhas in the feet.

DIANA » Do you think it is time to go beyond the Indian heritage or system and try to learn from everything we have around us today? That includes the Hollywood silent movies, nature, and everything else.

D O N A » Yes, I think so. We were talking about our homo-centric point of view and the ego-centric point of view and the cultural-centric point of view because each one looks out at life, at the universe, from their own con-centric point of view. Which is as a human being homo-centric, as a culture culture-centric, and as 'me' ego-centric. That is how we look outward. In a way, each one of us is the center of the universe, of life, because from all angles life pressurizes against us, pushes on us, like being in a house with many windows, and the trees outside are pushing into the windows. But I keep all my windows closed and keep only one open and I say: "I only want to see what I can see through this one window, because that is spiritual, that is good. The other windows I want to keep closed." But life, the universe, presses in from all sides. It knocks on the windows and says: "Hey, hey! Wake up! Open the window, I have got some goodies for you." And we say: "No, I do not want your goodies, I do not like what you have there, I want that one there." All our life we choose. We say: "I want this, but I do not want that." As if we know what we want. There is no way we can know what we want because we do not know what the goody is that is coming. To choose something and to reject something else is arbitrary and also tricky, because you can loose a lot of goodies that come in a roundabout way.

To come back to Fairbanks; I had never heard of him before. I had never watched silent movies before. I practice Head- and Shoulder balance every afternoon and I get bored, because it is twenty minutes Head balance everyday. You know, there you are, twenty minutes on your head. So I sometimes watch television. A couple of years ago I watched television in this way and the only program that was not utterly boring, which was not a talk show, was a program for children. At the end of this program they showed for twenty minutes of Zorro with Duncan Regeer as an educational program for children. I got intrigued with the idea of this Zorro figure, this nobleman, who wanted to help the poor Indios in California and

I told Toni about it. She said; "Oh, do not watch that one, you have to see the real one, the original one." I did not know what the original one was but went to the shop in Florence and I said to the shopkeeper: "I want the first Zorro movie that you have." He gave me one that had Tyrone Power in it. I phoned Toni and said: "I have got it." She said: "Which one is it?" And I said: "It is Tyrone Power." She said: "No, that is not the real one, the original one, you have to get the real one." So through various people I finally got a copy of the original movie, the one of Fairbanks. I had never heard the name before. I watched it; you have to get used to these 1920's movies, a lot of vaudeville action, a lot of body language, no talking, slightly corny from our point of view sometimes. I had to watch it a couple of times and then it really zoomed in on me, the way he moved. I thought: "Wait a minute, I have never seen this before, I am on to something that I can really use, this is revolutionary." I began to study his movements and integrate them the yoga. It made my yoga change.

DIANA » Don't you find it strange that you went through so much trouble to get to this movie just because you saw a children's program?

DONA » No, this is the beauty. We were talking about the quantum flirt the other day. Through watching TV in Head balance I came full circle back to yoga: It began with yoga and it ended with yoga through the silent movies. These things are very interesting, fun. Therefore I say that if you are snobbish and say: "Oh, movies are not spiritual, I can only learn from reading spiritual books." I would have missed the whole thing. I would never have got that movement. Once I got that, I could recognize glimpses of it in other people. For instance, one of my favorite dancers was Cyd Charisse. She had that movement; she was very plastic, smooth, driven in her movement - but inward driven, not outward driven. Most dancing is hot, not inward. If you watch flamenco dancers, you can see that the younger people are excited, so they throw it all out, but the older ones are not excited any more, because they have done it for forty, fifty, sixty years. All the energy is pulled inward; the whole power is pulled inward. It is very powerful to watch, very beautiful.

DIANA » Would you think that, if we were tuned to what is around us, we could integrate these synchronicities?

DONA » Each one of us is the center of the universe; you cannot get away from it. You cannot say: "I want to do this practice to get somewhere else." The universe is here, we are here, and we are the center of the universe. It is pushing on us all the time, knocking on the window, saying: "Knock, knock, open the window," so that eventually we may have that complete vision all around. That is the whole idea, to get us out of this enclosure that we are in so that we are part of the whole thing. But the tragic part of it is that we are taught to choose all the time. Our whole cultural, our whole human existence makes us choose. You say: "This is bad, this is good; this is up, this is down; this is left, this is right; this is spiritual, this is not spiritual." I was saying the other day that one building with a cross on top is a spiritual building. The other building with the neon sign of the casino on it is a bad building. These are man-made definitions, man-made choices. On a certain level they are necessary, because you have to live with the man-made definitions. But you should treat them with a lot of discretion, a lot of discrimination, knowing that they are only man-made. So when you say: "Movies are bad, TV is un-spiritual, you may miss a lot." The universe is knocking on our doors through documentaries, through movies, and we lose it. I watch a lot of movies and from each movie I get something. Another window opens and another. This is what we were saying about the eyes. Most people have a wall behind the eyes. You look into their eyes and there is a wall behind them, you bump into a wall. But the more windows are open, the more the house is open to all sides, when you look into the eyes there is endless space behind them, fields, and forests. There is a long range behind the eyes because the windows are open. The more the windows are closed the more there is a wall behind the eyes and you cannot go through them, there is no space, no field, no forests. The eyes with space have a spark, the walled-in ones do not.

DIANA » What is this spark?

DONA » It shows how many windows are open, how much you use the man-made structure but from outside, not from inside. What we were saying the other day is that these man-made structures - whether they are secular or religious - are vortexes. You go on the stream of life quite happily and then you meet a vortex and get sucked into this vortex, twirled around in it.

DIANA » You were talking about the Castaneda Journey to Ixtlan.

DONA » It is about a village, Ixtlan and a man who lives there, Don Genaro. One day he gets picked up by a force - what Castaneda calls an 'ally' - and gets spun around and in this spinning he is taken away from his village. When he finally stops spinning he does not know where he is. He wants to go back home but does not know the direction. So he begins to walk in the direction that he thinks his village is and he meets some people on the way. He asks them: "Where is Ixtlan?" and they say: "Oh, we are going there. You can come with us." He joins them and they start to walk in a certain direction, but after a while they sit down and pull out some sandwiches. He says: "What are you doing?" and they say: "We are going to eat now. You want to join us? Here is food." At that he feels the hair on his neck prickly, picks up his bag and runs away scared. Again he meets other people and says: "Where is Ixtlan?" And they say: "Oh, we are going there, you can join us. We can show you the way." He joins them and they too after a while pull out food and offer the food to him. This happens a couple of times and each time that the people offer him food he gets scared and runs away. Castaneda asks if in the end Don Genaro found his way back to Ixtlan and Don Juan says: "No, he never found his way back. He is still on the road." This symbolizes for me that we have lost the universe, life. We meet people on the road, which are those vortexes, and they say: "If you join us we are going to take you back." So you get into the vortex but there is no way you can get out. That is why you get scared; you get out, and continue on your way till the next vortex. The art is to try to circumvent all these vortexes and keep going in the direction that you think you are going, which means that you are not being sucked into any system, any structure.

DIANA » Any system or any person that promises something is a vortex?

DONA » Exactly. The vortex is the promise, the promise of the reward, of paradise, of enlightenment, of better times, of 'the grass is greener over the hill'. It is the promise that either the person or the system makes to get you to Ixtlan. This promise is the vortex that sucks you in because of your fears. You are so afraid of losing the reward, that even if the promise never comes true you will hang on, because maybe one day it will come true. That is where you get sucked in and then it is very difficult to get out of it.

The vortex that sucks us in is any system, guru, or person, that makes the promise, that gives you the promise of taking you back to Ixtlan. That is basically the story of Journey to Ixtlan. The food is the symbol of the promise: "We are having lunch now and then we are going to Ixtlan." Again you are caught in the time and space situation of the mind that says that through a time sequencing, through a system, you are going 'home', to 'Ixtlan'. But in the meanwhile you are losing life all around you because you are looking over the hill, over the horizon, hoping the grass will be greener there, because somebody told you it will. So what is on this side all around you, you lose it, you lose it completely.

I like watching movies because you can get so much out of just very small pieces. I saw one movie with Burt Reynolds, a western. It is quite violent at certain times. Some bandits rob a train and by chance there is a rich woman who is running away from her husband. She witnesses the robbery and so they kidnap her with her umbrella, her beautiful clothes and her beautiful horse. In the next couple of days they rape her, they steal her possessions, they do all kinds of horrible things to her. Then they kill each other. The only ones who stay alive in the end is the leader of the gang, Burt Reynolds and she. By that time she has lost her horse, she has lost her clothes, she has lost her umbrella. She is dressed in a poncho, a horse blanket, she has a straw hat on her head, she is riding a mule, and she is riding behind this man. She does not know where she is going, she does not know where she is, she does not know who he is, she does not know his name, she does not know anything. They ride through this beautiful landscape, the flowers, the trees, and the mountains - like the Grand Tetons. Suddenly he hears her laugh and he turns around to look at her. She is on this mule and she is singing and laughing, exploding with joy. You know that in that moment she realized that she had lost everything, that she had nothing more to lose. Suddenly the whole world is wide open, she sees the mountains, the flowers, the man in front of her; the whole world is completely fresh, new. It is an explosion that is really very moving to see. So you can get those glimpses anywhere.

DIANA » The things that we are attached to, the systems, the goals, are something heavy that we carry. They prevent us from exploding, enjoying the moment?

DONA » We have to use things, we have to use the man-made world. But if we are hanging on to that and if that again carries the promise of something better then that is the vortex, the attachment. It is the attachment to the things that we have, not the things in themselves. In that moment that she was laughing she realized that she was free. She could not do it while she had her beautiful clothes, her beautiful horse, her parasol. For her it could only happen when she realized that she had lost everything.

There is another movie called Stolen Hours, kind of a La Traviata story. It is the story of a rich society woman who discovers that she is dying of cancer. She marries her doctor and they go and live in a little village on the coast of Ireland. She knows exactly how much time she has: eight months. At the end of the eight months she will just drop dead one day but she does not know which day. So she has the choice to either be sorry for herself, go into therapy, be miserable; or use the time as best as she can. The whole movie is about how she uses that time. She gets out, makes friends with the whole village, becomes the heart and soul of the whole village, of the children. She has parties, they go to the beach, they play. Every second of her life becomes extremely precious, full of life, fun, joy, and beauty. She knows that time is running out and because time is running out she has time to enjoy life. Most of us have unconsciously the idea that we are immortal, we never die. In Italian they have a proverb that says: "Everybody has to die, maybe even I." "Maybe," ... "maybe" ... There is always in our mind somewhere that, maybe even I... but maybe not, maybe I do not have to die. So we think we can afford to take time, which is a phantom idea because, of course, we are going to die. We do not know when, but we are. Instead of saying, like in that movie: "OK, I have this time only, afterward the whole show is over, I am going to really enjoy the whole thing, get out there and take every moment as it comes." In another Castaneda book there is a sentence where it says to the extend that 'sorcery' is taking off the mask which makes you see the world as monotonous and repetitious and putting on the other mask which makes you see the world for what it really is, a transitory blooming of something incredible which happens only once in the life of the universe and will never be repeated again. This is exactly it: we have no time, we cannot afford to be bored. Every leaf that falls has never fallen that way in the history of the world and it will never fall in the same way afterward. Everything, every moment is totally unique and separate from the past and the future. So if you are so busy looking through a system at some future reward then this whole incredible show is just out of your range.

DIANA » That is why we get bored?

DONA » That is why we get bored. We get bored because we think that we have time, we think that the tree is always the same, we think that the house is always the same. It is not. It is never the same. The atoms, the molecules, everything is always in motion. The tree is never the same, the animal is never the same. But we look only very superficially and we see more or less the same dog shape everyday and so we think it is the same dog, but it is not the same dog. If we look with those old eyes we get bored. But if we look with young eyes - with the eyes of innocence - everything is new, it has never happened before and it will never happen afterwards. Then there is a lot of excitement because everything is beautiful, everything is fun, everything is alive, on the one hand eternal, and on the other hand ephemeral, it has never happened before and it will never happen again. This is the balance between the eternal and the time-bound; unique and eternal at the same time.

DIANA » You said that you knew many yoga people who did not watch television or films because that is not spiritual. Do you think there is this false connection between being spiritual and not having any fun, just being serious and forgetting all the fun things? Because I think most people enjoy going to the movies. Why do these people who follow the so-called spiritual path believe they have to stop having fun?

DONA » Frankly speaking, I do not know myself. I can only say it is what we have been talking about: the house with the windows, and people have the idea that you can only get your spirituality through one window, through a certain channel. We only choose one channel. Whatever comes through the channel is taken seriously and everything else is rejected. It is again choosing between all the different things, choosing which one, according to you, is spiritual and helpful. There is the proverb that says 'beauty is in the eye of the beholder'. I think the same thing goes for sacredness, spirituality. Everything is in the eye of the beholder, beauty, ugliness, and sacredness; everything is in the eye of the beholder. Things in themselves, things or ideas, are not spiritual or ugly or beautiful.

They are what you perceive them to be. To the despondent everything looks gloomy, to the spiritual everything has a spiritual meaning. It depends on you. The thing outside, whether it is an idea, a philosophy, a tree, a house: it touches you from outside and then we bounce the ball back. We bounce the ball back with our judgment. We say the house is not sacred but the Buddha statue is sacred. They are both only things: a house is a house and a Buddha statue is a Buddha statue, there is nothing sacred or ugly about it. But we bounce the ball back loaded with our judgment. That is how we choose all the time instead of letting the universe, life, things, come to us; just let them come inside and see what they do to us. Then there is a very different relationship. Depending on our inner receptivity, our inner cleanliness, or clarity of perception, everything is spiritual. You cannot divide life and the universe in half and say: "This half is spiritual and this half is not spiritual." Because you get in to an incredible tangle there of who is the one who made the un-spiritual path or the un-spiritual things? You get in to a real messy tangle. Everything is spiritual, because everything has a value of teaching you something.

DIANA » Including the Fairbanks movies.

DONA » Including any movie. It depends on where you are inside yourself, on which point you are in your own development. When we are walking on our path in life each moment we are open for something. Today I may be open for this thing and tomorrow I may be open for something else. We do not know where that opening is going to be filled or with what. That is why we always have to be on the alert, we have to be fast, alert, to catch it, to fill that opening, that hole in the place where I am now, so that all the time we are more and more open inside.

DIANA » The teaching is everywhere.

DONA » The teaching is absolutely everywhere. Everything, every leaf that falls is a teacher, every movie you see is a teacher, every song you hear is a teacher, every bird that flies is a teacher. But it depends on you with what kind of eyes you look. If you look with eyes that are bored and say: "Oh, that movie, oh, that bird flying, oh, those clouds…" If you look with eyes that are tired and old and bored then you lose everything, but if you look with eyes that are fresh and new and see everything as an ephemeral happening then everything is a teacher.

DIANA » You were talking about collecting the energy inward, the cohesion of the body.

DONA » Normally we throw the movement outside and so the body is moving in all directions. It is not together. The real control is when all the movement, all the energy, is pulled inward, collected together, put together; then, as one unit, you move forward into the movement. In this way the body is not fragmented. Most of the time we are fragmented in our movements. It is seldom that you have a movement that involves the whole body. When I saw this kind of control in the flamenco dancing, in Fairbanks and others, I thought: "How can you get the energy to come together, inside." Therefore I got interested in the idea of the bandhas. The body has a particular structure - the human structure. It has the skeleton, the joints, the bones, the muscles, and the arches. If we do not take the body as a structured unit into consideration then we move in a fragmented way. But the body does have certain pathways that are very smooth. They form, as it were, a landscape. In a natural landscape you may have mountains like the Tetons with a river meandering through them. It does not crash through but goes around the mountains. The body also has certain pathways and if you follow those pathways the movement can be fast, smooth, or slow, but going through these natural pathways of the body they are beautiful, cohesive, harmonious, because they follow the natural pathways of the body.

The bandhas are a way of guiding the movement from arch to arch: from the foot arch, from the ankles, up into the hip joints, the pelvic diaphragm; from there up into the lower thoracic diaphragm and then it flows out through the arm movement. Thus there is a coherence in the movement because it follows a natural arch pathway and also a natural muscular pathway; through a particular muscle chain which then carries the spark of the movement very smoothly from muscle to muscle. If, on the other hand, you use - quote/unquote - the 'wrong muscle' then the movement gets stuck there, and then you have to pull it out of that muscle to go somewhere else. But if you follow the natural pathway then the spark will jump over each time by itself, it does not get stuck in that one area. Therefore touching the beginning point of the pathway the whole pathway will suddenly flow by itself.

DIANA » This is very close to projecting the energy first.

DONA » Yes, it has to do with projecting the energy. Movement is energy but in general the brain and the movement go together, almost at the same time. The brain gives the command to the muscle to move, but what moves the brain? What somebody like Fairbanks learned to do, and what I have learned to do too, is to use visualization to move the brain, to create a gap in which you move the image a fraction of a second before you actually move the body. The projection that you make of the movement is faster than the body and so it pulls the body. Therefore you are not pushing the body through a movement but allowing the body to be pulled by the image, by the projection.

DIANA » Does it have to do with inhabiting your own body at all times?

DONA » Exactly. We come back to that full attention. It is to be attentive of your body at all times; your attention fills the whole body. Many people who do dancing or acrobatics may be very attentive in the moment of their act, but once the performance is over they are back to the normal state of inattention. What I found extraordinarily attractive and fun in the Fairbanks movies was that there was no break between: now we are in the gym with gym clothes on and now we are in normal life with normal clothes on. In any movie he could walk in the street in a three piece suit, in a tuxedo, a high hat, and shining five hundred dollar shoes; and suddenly, before you know where you are, he is running up the wall of a house and climbing into the third floor window, tuxedo and all. No division between: now we are doing gymnastics, climbing walls or trees, and now we are being normal, walking in a three piece suit in the street, the way most people divide their activities. Gymnasts do their thing in the gym hall, and then they have a shower, go home and are 'normal' again. The overlapping of the full bodily attention and motion with – quote/unquote – 'normal life' is extremely attractive and funny. It needs full attention in the body to be always aware of what you are doing. Most people just collapse under the weight gravity, losing the attention in the body. It is interesting, valuable and beautiful to all the time inhabit your body to the full extent with full awareness, full attention, full joy; inhabiting it all the time, not only at certain times.

DIANA » Being more flexible with defining what is your practice and what is not your practice?

DONA » Exactly. You turn everything into a practice. I heard that there was one movie of Fairbanks where he went on a huge cruise boat and practically turned the whole cruise boat into a gym. The whole movie is about how he jumps over railings, slides down the stairs and jumps up the stairs using the whole boat as a gym to show that anything that you encounter can be used to enhance your bodily proficiency, your bodily efficiency, and just the use of furniture for exercise can be a fun thing. You do not need only to sit on a chair. You can also jump over it, somersault over it, do handstand on it; you can do all kinds of things with it. In this way you can widen your range of tools by just using anything you encounter, which is a liberating feeling and has a liberating effect. You do not 'have' to use things in a predetermined way only for that purpose because society tells you to. You can turn anything into a toy, for anything you want.

DIANA » Like children.

DONA » Like children. You do not have to get stuck in a rut of this thing is to be used for this and that thing is to be used for that; this piece of furniture is for this and that one is for that. You can play around without getting stuck in your mind. It is a mental flexibility too, that you do not 'have' to sit on the chair but that you can do something else with it too. You do not 'have' to only do one thing with the things around you. You are free to do lots of things, whatever you want. This is the inner flexibility, the inner freedom.

D O N A » I once saw a documentary of a Friesian horse, a huge black stallion. He was being filmed and he knew it too, running towards the camera, running out again, his mane flying, his tail flying, putting on this huge show for the camera, not at all meek or timid or humble; he was all out there, really all out there. It was mind-blowing, the way he was doing that, so full of joie de vivre, so full of his own power, his beauty, his speed. He knew that everybody is important in the universe, that we should not be humble and meek and low profile. We should be out there and express our joie de vivre, our being.

D O N A » When you watch the flamenco dancers, especially the old women who have danced for many years, probably a whole lifetime, you can see how the movement has been driven inward. In the beginning when they just start everything is thrown outside, the movement, the energy, the power. Then the art is to repeat, repeat, repeat, repeat the movement until gradually we pull the movement inside the body and internalize the movement inside the body. To pull it all inside and keep it all together needs, in the first place, a lot of practice; but it also it needs the mind: it needs attention. Repeating movements without full attention has no lasting value. You have to pay full attention to your movement.

People always talk about practice and discipline as something which is imposed from outside. You are here and then out there is the discipline or the practice. I think that that is the wrong approach because it is dualistic.

The word 'interest', to be interested in something comes from the Latin verb 'to be inside'. In 'interest' the mind is completely inside.

When you are 'interested' in what you are doing you do not need discipline, you do not need practice, you do not need force because you are 'inside'. You do not need somebody else to tell you to do it. It is a very interesting, powerful way of doing it in which you need mind and body, not merely mindless repetition. Some people are really inside their body. They are passionately, fiercely 'interested' in what they are doing. Their interest, their mental power, their mental attention, fills the whole body from the inside, nothing in the body is empty. It is filled from the inside by attention. What we were talking about yesterday on the hike is that the word concentration means to 'zoom in' on something. Concentration belongs to the continuous mind. The continuous mind can concentrate, but it can never be attentive because attention is outside its domain. Attention in the movement or in looking comes from somewhere else; it is something that the body does. It is a reaching out of the body to touch that quantum thing out there; it is the quantum flirt, the quantum touch with the world around us. That quantum touch goes through the cells of the body, the atoms of the body, the material of the body, and through the heart; not the emotional heart but the real heart as an organ of intelligence. You have two hearts, the emotional heart which derives its energy from the past, and the real one which functions outside the space/time confinement. The emotional heart has personal memory as is being proven by many heart transplant surgeons who are doing tests on their patients. It works together with the thinking mind - you have a thought and you get emotional about it. But the real heart, which does not deal with personal memory, is capable of having that quantum touch, touching the tree, watching the bird. It deals with the moment of total attention when you and the bird are in the same space. That 'being in the same space at the same time' takes place through the inner heart. You can see in dancers that that is where the whole power is, not in concentration, not in the mind, but in the interest that brings you in touch with the movement and so with the inner heart of it.

DIANA » That is where the power comes from.

DONA » That is where the real power comes from. There are different gradations of power, different levels of power: there is muscle power, and so, sometimes in dance, when the dancers are wild, they throw power out and once it is out it is lost. That is the typical muscle power. It gets thrown out and is lost. While the power that comes from being passionately interested is inward, it does not get thrown out. I like words that are derived from Latin, because if you go back to the original meaning it is very interesting. For instance, the word 'passionate' originally comes from 'passion', which means 'suffering'. The quantum touch is like a suffering in the sense that it touches you in the deepest core. It is painful, but it is a painfulness, which is a beautiful, explosive thing. Sometimes the movements of horses and other animals can be beautiful in the sense of heartbreaking; so beautiful that it almost hurts.

DIANA » Can that trigger an emotion?

DONA » No. That kind of thing falls outside the emotions, outside thinking, outside the continuous mind, which are all in one space. This kind of fierce passion, this heartbreaking thing, this quantum touch, belongs to the quantum mind. It is in a different space, the two are separate and they cannot overlap.

DIANA » Maybe the emotion is this part that always wants to come back and take over.

DONA » Yeah, the emotion is something that you throw back at the things. Something hits you: a tree, or a bird, or a dance; it hits you, and what you throw back is the emotion. But if you do not throw back an emotion, when you allow the outer thing to touch the inside, then that is a different thing. That is that quantum touch, that real heart thing.

DIANA » I am interested in the power and the strength, the power inside.

DONA » When the power is inside you have control over it. When the power is outside you lose it. What people call power is in general a very superficial thing. Inner power is when you sit comfortably in the 'real' world, the quantum world, then you have the real power. The external power is the action you take to cover up an inner lack of power.

DIANA » How do you recognize this thing that some dancers have and some do not.

DONA » Not only dancers. Anything that you touch, you recognize it. I do not know how, but it is done through the eyes, through the body, through the heart. It is the effect of that total attention and that quality of the movement, in what degree that movement was done in a timeless state. I think that timelessness recognizes timelessness. If you are in the same state of mind you can recognize it. Before we were talking about helping each other and teaching and we were saying you cannot teach another.

Remember this video with the Friesian horse which was so powerful, so joyful; this huge black horse with the flying mane, the flying tail? He knew he was being filmed and he was running around the fields, absolutely glorious, magnificent, one explosion of joy, and fun and that is the teaching. That joy has the capacity to jump over. That is why we said yesterday that you cannot teach, you cannot help, you cannot even be an example; you can only be what you are, and what you are will jump over.

DIANA » Do you think that a film is as powerful an image of whoever is in a film as the real thing in front of you?

DONA » I think so. Beauty is in the eye of the beholder. Everything depends on you; not on the movie, not on the animal, not on the dance; it depends on you, what you can recognize. Many people may look at these flamenco dancers and not see anything at all apart from a fat woman twirling around. They would not be able to see the power because it is not in them. Seeing is always recognizing. You cannot see what is not inside yourself, that is impossible. You can only see what is inside yourself. Seeing, which is looking, is always a recognition. If something is not in yourself you will not see it.

Some people see badness everywhere: people are bad, animals are bad, everything is bad. These things are in yourself, not in people; the 'badness' as something that you recognize on the outside is inside yourself. You can only see in other things what is inside yourself. Again we come back to 'beauty is in the eyes of the beholder'. If there is no beauty inside yourself you cannot recognize it outside.

DIANA » Is it archetypal?

DONA » It is archetypal, that is why you can recognize it. There are certain moments, but not everybody has that opening to receive that moment. If you have that opening, then anything can come and you can catch it, can recognize it because it is not only for you; it is archetypal.

Eyes of Innocence
Dona Holleman

5   Interview at the Million Dollar Cowboy Bar

T O N I » (*lifting her wine glass*) To life.

D O N A » To life and to horses and cowboys. You were telling me the other day that you had a story from New Zealand about horses.

T O N I » Yes, my million-dollar horse story... this is long time ago. The kids and I were in New Zealand and we were going to do a four-five day trip. But Michelle wanted to go horseback riding because she loves to ride. So the day before we were going to go on this trail ride. I wanted to go just for half a day, but she said: "No, no." She wanted to go for the whole day so they put me on this horse which had quite a broad back and the man who brought me on the horse said: "Now if the saddle starts to shift a little bit, all you have to do is..." [*laughing*] So here we are single file on this narrow trail with on the left side a wall and on the right side it dropped down... way down, and way down below you could see this river with boats. And of course the saddle was shifting in...

D O N A » You were going like that...

T O N I » ... in the downhill direction. [*laughing*] What else... people behind me were saying; "Jump off, jump off!" I mean, I wasn't in any position to jump off; the trail was too narrow and I didn't have the nerve... Anyway, so I just kept leaning towards the hill. And when we got to an open place, there was a guide at the front and a guide at the back, and the guide at the back caught me just as... [*laughing*] just as I was rolling off the saddle. What had happened was that this horse had been put on a diet [*laughing*] and they didn't cinch the whatever it is that they cinch up tight enough so he did that. I was fine for the rest of the trip until, well... we went halfway and had lunch and the people that were just going for half a day went back, but we continued on. It was a great ride; but as we returned to the ranch I just couldn't find any way to sit comfortably anymore and I suddenly realized that this isn't unusual, but even at that time which was a long time ago, I was the oldest person on this trip and I thought: "What are you doing?" "Why are you doing this?" The kids laughed at me because I couldn't sit down, I could hardly sit down for dinner. And the next day we were going to start hiking...

D O N A » That was your life as a cowboy.

T O N I » That was my life as a cowboy.

D O N A » It didn't last very long, did it?

T O N I » But when we started hiking I was fine.

D O N A » You are more of a walker.

T O N I » Than a rider, yes.

D O N A » I think that riding is important. The problem with yoga is that we are always so much alone with ourselves. You have your yoga mat and you are just sitting there doing your thing. You do not have to pay attention to anybody, you do not have to take care of anybody; it is very introverted, self-centered. This reflects on us in the yoga world. What I learned in horse riding is that when there are two of you there is a symbiosis.

T O N I » Hopefully.

D O N A » No, not hopefully because that horse can throw you off unless you pay attention.

T O N I » Right, that is what I mean: 'hopefully'...

D O N A » Yeah, because unless you pay attention and go exactly with the horse's movements he is going to kick you off sooner or later, which happened regularly with me. But, apart from that, it is really a great tool for paying attention. All the martial arts have this potentiality of teaching you to pay attention to the other, because they too are involved. There is a kind of dance together, you can trip each other up; the horse can trip you up.

T O N I » It is like fencing... you have to be alert, otherwise you can be...

D O N A » Yeah, and so it is a tremendous tool to teach you alertness if you want to use it as a tool like that. The thing I like about horse riding is that you can apply it to your own body. A horse is a living thing, and if you are on the horse you are dealing with a living thing, so there should also be that feeling of dealing with something alive. If you turn it around and use it for your own body and say: "I am dealing with ideas, but I am also dealing with my personal horse which is my body." Therefore you have to really take care of your personal horse to make sure that it feels comfortable.

T O N I » That you are not overdoing it.

D O N A » Just before I came to America to make this movie I was in the airport. There was a big television screen and they were showing dressage championship. There was this huge black Friesian stallion, which is anyway...

T O N I » They are so gorgeous...

D O N A » If you are talking about elegance incarnate you are talking about a Friesian stallion. There he was with this woman on his back and they were doing this dance, the dressage dance. It was mind-blowing because usually when you see somebody sit in the saddle you know that there is a horse and there is a saddle and there is a person. But with this horse and woman it was as if there was only one thing, not a horse, not a saddle and not a woman. What you saw was a horsewoman indivisible. It was like watching a dance, or watching flamenco. The whole movement was so smooth, so beautiful; and the rhythm of the horse, even in very slow motion, was just incredible. It was so controlled and so beautiful. You can really learn from these animals. If you use your eyes and watch the beauty of the movement, that inward control of the movement.

T O N I » They have a natural grace.

T O N I » OK Dona, here we are in the Million Dollar Cowboy Bar in...

D O N A » Jackson Hole, Wyoming.

T O N I » Right, and we are drinking wine and having a great time sitting on saddles. What do you think about all that?

D O N A » Well, I think it is great.

T O N I » Yeah, isn't it? Lots of fun?

D I A N A » Should a yogi be in the Cowboy bar?

D O N A » Well, let us ask it this way: What is a yogi? I am not a yogi.

D I A N A » Why not?

D O N A » Because if you call yourself a yogi you are again compart-mentalizing, you are again fragmenting. Nobody is born a yogi, nobody is born a cowboy. We are born babies, human babies; and you become a yogi, you become a cowboy, you become whatever it is. Again this same division all the time, we are born human beings; then, within the whole six billion range of the human beings you say, I'm an American human being. How many million Americans...?

T O N I » You just do not want to be limited, you do not want to be...

D O N A » Yeah, you limit yourself; then you limit yourself more, then you limit yourself more, then you are a protestant American, then you are a protestant cowboy American, then you are a protestant yogi cowboy American; so all the time you are putting yourself in smaller and smaller boxes.

T O N I » Exactly.

D O N A » That is constricting.

T O N I » It is. So how do you think of yourself?

D O N A » Not as a yogi; as a human being.

T O N I » No, no, no. Rather than a negative, how do you think of yourself positively?

D O N A » As a human being

T O N I » OK.

D O N A » That is bad enough, because if you say: "I am a human being," it means: "I am not an elk, I am not a moose."

T O N I » You are not an elk, and you are not a moose. At least I have not seen the horns.

D O N A » I do have them [laughing]. But I am cutting out all those things; I am taking myself out of a large range of life.

T O N I » Well, yes, but...

D O N A » It is only an idea, not a real thing.

T O N I » Exactly, but you cannot say: "I am a cougar."

D O N A » No.

T O N I » Because you are not a cougar.

D O N A » I am a human being, but if I say: "I am a yogi", then that very word 'yogi' is the vortex. Because it is not only a word. With the word comes a whole bag of rules and regulations: yogis do not drink wine, yogis do not go to Cowboy Bars, yogis do this, yogis do that... You get a whole bag of 'dos' and 'don'ts' and those are arbitrary.

T O N I » For some people.

D I A N A » Is this a spiritual place?

D O N A » What?

DIANA » The cowboy bar.

DONA » It depends on you. A place is neither spiritual nor not-spiritual. There is not a sign in the universe which says: "This building is a non-spiritual building" and on another building: "This is a spiritual building." The signs are put on them by human beings. If you are not spiritual, it is very hard to find spiritual things in life. This is the problem, that a lot of people shut out a lot of things by saying: "That is not spiritual." How do we know? Who says so? The one who says so is me, and what do I know? It is only man made decisions...

TONI » You make the judgments...

DONA » It is back to judgments again.

DIANA » Would you like a yoga teacher who would not let you drink red wine?

TONI » I do not think I would have a yoga teacher who would not let me drink red wine. I do not like to be told what to do.

DONA » I would like Toni not to have a yoga teacher at all. Each one of us is our own teacher.

TONI » I do not have a yoga teacher.

DONA » Exactly.

TONI » It comes right down to it.

DONA » Because the moment you have a yoga teacher... we are all teaching yoga...

TONI » But I have a friend.

DONA » We are all teaching yoga but again, if you say you are a teacher, you create a small vortex; a teacher is only a teacher if he has students, otherwise he is not a teacher. A student is only a student if he has a teacher. So again you get into this kind of little dance, little vortex, where it is very easy to create a co-dependency situation.

TONI » That is why Dona never wanted people to so-called 'follow her'. Dona always encouraged them to be independent, to do their own thing.

DONA » We come back to the same thing, what we were saying before. You can only do your thing and then somebody may look on and say: "Hey, that looks good, I want to have as much fun and be as free as that." Then they can do it, but it is their responsibility. You are only responsible to be what you are, that is all. Then the other person can take the baton or not, you have nothing to do with it. It is none of your business what the other person does. So as a yoga teacher you just say: "OK do this, do this." But whether the other person takes it or not is out of your range.

D O N A » I think we are getting tired, we are getting really silly.

T O N I » That is good, I like being silly.

D O N A » So we should not stop having fun.

T O N I » No!

D O N A » You go on with your question. What is the next question?

D I A N A » The fun thing.

T O N I » If we are going to be serious, depressed, and all of those awful things... what a drag. Nobody wants you around. You do not enjoy anything: you do not enjoy yourself, you do not enjoy anybody else, you do not enjoy life; that is not the way to be. People respond to you more if you are joyful, if you enjoy things. And even if you do not care whether other people respond to you or not, you enjoy because you feel better.

D I A N A » Do you think that sometimes people in the yoga world stop having fun and take it too seriously?

T O N I » I do not know. I do not think that we should get into denying either. I get tired sometimes and I get miserable sometimes and it is OK. I know that the fatigue and the depression is super-ficial; but underneath it I know that I am OK, just OK. So I think we should not be too strict in trying to be happy; just let things relax. If you relax into things, it softens the edges. It is the same in yoga. Often people say: "Oh, I have a shoulder that hurts, what can I do, and they try to run away from it, they try to cure it, they try to do this, they try to do that." This is a very aggressive approach. The whole approach is geared to deny the pain and to run away from it, to cure it. On the other hand, if you just relax, just let it be, go with it, just look at it, sit, as it were, next to your sore shoulder, just sit there, then the sharp edges go off, they disappear. The sore is there, but it is mellow, it is OK. It is not OK as long as you try to run away from it, it becomes sharp. But if you do not run away and do not try to 'do' something all the time, it is OK, it mellows out.

T O N I » There is a wonderful story about a centipede that had arthritis. He went to all the critters in the forest to get advice as to what he should do about his sore legs. The advice from one was: "Chop off the leg." The other animal said: "Do more exercise." Another one told him to take a kind of tonic or herbs, and this went on and on and on, until he did not have many legs left. Finally he went to the owl, and the owl said very wisely: "Concentrate on the well leg." Instead of bringing all your emphasis where it hurts.

D O N A » Yeah. I think that it is a very western approach anyway, to deny and run away... Remember that time in Bali. There was this young boy, and he had had a bicycle accident. His whole arm was a real bloody mess. We were saying: "Oh, poor boy, how did you do that?" We were all, you know, western compassion. And this boy looked at us as if we were totally crazy and began to laugh hysterically and said: "What are you worried about? It is only a cut arm, nothing else." I mean, he thought we were nuts being worried about his arm and saying: "Oh, poor guy, how are you doing?", all compassion and stuff. He could not care less.

T O N I » He was just going on with his life.

D O N A » He was just going on with his life, he just had a cut arm and that was it. There was nothing to worry about or get upset about or get emotional about. This whole emotional spiel around a hurt is typical for a soft western culture.

D I A N A » Can you speak about the denial? Do you think it is bad to deny, to discipline thinking that if you are going to lead a healthy life you are not suppose to have coffee and stay up all night?

D O N A » I think that the body and mind are like a small child. If you tell the child: "Don't do this!" the temptation to do that, right there is just overwhelming and he will end up doing that. I think the 'don't do this' does not work, the denial does not work. As Toni says we have to work on the positive side, not go into the 'don't do' thing, but go more into the 'being interested' thing.

т о n i » To enjoy.

d o n a » To enjoy and to be interested in what you are doing, not deny, because the denial will only create a backlash, which means that you want it more that before. It is like: "Don't eat ice cream." Of course afterwards your mind is obsessed with eating ice cream, all you can think about is eating ice cream.

Eyes of Innocence
Dona Holleman

6   Interview at Margo's studio

DIANA » What is the aim of the yoga postures?

DONA » I am not quite sure whether it is a general question. I think that many people have a certain aim before doing yoga. You can tie three concepts together in that one question: denial, reward, and attention. It is a triangular situation. We live in a society that toggles back and forth between denial and the reward. We never act only for the sake of acting; we always act either to get out of a situation, to deny that situation, or to get a reward, or preferably both. Many people come to yoga in order to get away from a situation that they do not like, for instance, a physical problem, a disease, a mental problem or just fatigue. They want to get away from that situation and achieve health, well-being, the reward, a better future, and they think yoga is going to do all that. Most likely it will; but it is not really the main issue of yoga. Yoga is not a practice in order to get a reward. If you do feel better afterwards, you do get health, you do get benefits, those are side products, they are never the main issue. The denial is when we have a physical problem or a mental problem, and we do not want to deal with it directly. We want to get away from it, we want to retreat from it. The retreat includes therapies, ways to see if we can escape from the present situation. It includes practice, it includes time, it includes a certain running away. This means that we never stay directly with the problem itself, but we deal with the means of getting away from it. Therefore we never understand the problem, why it came, why we got into this situation. We do not really deal with cause and effect; we deal with a way of escaping. We do not deal with how the situation developed in that way. We live in a society that always looks for a reward. You never do something just for the fun of doing it or for the sake of just doing it. We always do things with a goal in mind and the goal is always somewhere in the future. The goal is always - hopefully - brighter than the present. So we always work towards the reward, also in yoga. Thus we are either busy retreating backwards, away from the problem; or moving forward, toward the reward. Both these cases include time and time includes a whole process. Therefore we never come to a position of stand still. The position of stand still is only possible or only happens when you pay total attention in the moment. The asanas of course can have, on a superficial level, all kinds of side effects, beneficial effects, but I think that to see those only is a pity. The main focus in practicing the asanas is to pay attention and this attention means that there is no time involved.

There is no future, no reward involved and there is no retreating involved. It is just to be in that present moment. If you do that then, if there is a physical problem, being with it in the present moment, not retreating from it and not trying to solve the problem but being with it, staying with it will soften the boundaries of that problem. Then either it will disappear gradually or you can deal with it, because there is no emotional fallout about it. The retreat is an emotional thing, I want to get away from it, I want the reward. But just to stay with it, to just watch it and see how it develops, see how it softens is not an emotional thing. It is the attention thing and that is very different. So it is attention again. Attention and an emotional retreat or advance situation do not go together; it is an either/or situation. When you pay attention to the posture as it comes, as the body is doing it, it is very beautiful because the body can speak for itself in that moment. As long as you are retreating or advancing it means that the body is not heard. The body has its own language, its own needs, its own rules, its own moment of good or not feeling good. The body will tell you that and the body will tell you that in that posture. But as long as we are emotionally retreating or advancing, we cannot hear the body, therefore there will always be a gap between our intention of the posture and the posture itself, which is the body. It is never harmonious.

DIANA » Expecting something from yoga and the denial is considering yoga as a tool?

DONA » In that way yoga is a tool. As I say, yoga can bring benefits. It does bring benefits undoubtedly. Every physical activity that we do from swimming and football to yoga and dance has a negative and a positive side. The negative is the damaging side, let us say, the damaging of the body, and the beneficial side is what is good for the body. For instance, in some very violent sports like football and soccer obviously the damaging side is bigger and therefore the body breaks down sooner. When these boys get to the age of thirty, for a soccer or a football player the age of thirty is already old. For dance the beneficial side may be wider than the damaging side so dancers can continue till they are fifty, some even till they are sixty years old. As a physical activity yoga has a very large beneficial side and obviously a much narrower damaging side, so therefore as a system, as a beneficial system, yoga is quite unequaled. It is a total practice for the body in all directions. You can do forward bending, backbends, sideways, upside down, there is a lot of variety possible for the body, and it is always from the center to the periphery. Whatever moves from the center towards the periphery is beneficial. What comes from the periphery toward the center is harsh on the body. If you are in tension you crawl into yourself. The face frowns, you make the body small, retreating it from the periphery to the center. When you are happy, laughing and lying on the beach you open the body out from the center to the periphery. That is the beneficial side. Yoga has a lot of movements from the center, from the bone structure, towards the external structure, elongating further and further outwards. In that way, sure, yoga is a very beneficial thing to do, an all round practice to do. But, as I say, as long as there is the future reward involved in it and you are doing it for the future reward you are missing the present moment. It is like that tunnel sequence that we did: you are going through the tunnel and you are so busy getting to the other end of the tunnel. The grass is green there, there is a lot of light there, and you want to get to the other end of the tunnel, so you miss what is on the inside. To be totally attentive to the body means that you are interested in the body and in the movement. 'Interest' in Latin, as we said before, means 'to be inside'. It is the moment of being inter-ested, being 'inside' the movement or the posture as the posture unfolds that makes it complete. There is no future reward and no retreating involved, but it is only the moment as it is there. So the body is completely filled with the mind. The mind fills the body completely from the bone structure to the skin structure, while as long as there is a future reward the mind is very small within the skin and so there is a lot of empty space in the body.

DIANA » Making this effort to reach something is preventing us from being in that moment, fully present?

DONA » Exactly. As long as we make a lot of effort to do something for a reward. Now you can see effort in two different ways. If I make a lot of effort in a posture because I have to reach some future, fantastic, perfect posture, then I am never going to reach the perfect posture to start with, because that does not exist. So I will always move towards a phantom future; that is the effort that I use to move there. On the other hand you can also see effort in a different way, that it is a lot of fun sometimes to do a lot of effort. It feels good to make a big effort for something; not to reach something else but just for the fun of doing the effort, just to be with it. It feels nice to get tired sometimes. It is nice to climb up a mountain or go for a long hike and you get really tired and there is a lot of effort, but there is no future involved. You just do it because the body wants to make a big effort at that moment and it feels good to be tired. When you come home you have a nice dinner, you have a nice bath, and you feel good. That is the different side of effort, it is pure effort for its own sake. But if effort has a goal in order to reach something else then it is a little twisted.

DIANA » When you say not to deny the problem but to deal with it, there is some kind of responsibility, you say: "Why is the problem there in the first place?" Is choice something that has to do with our problems, our personal choice as human beings?

DONA » The responsibility is definitely ours. In denial we do not want to take responsibility for what is the problem. Sometimes we chose, but the choice may be so deep down and unconscious that we are not even aware that it is a choice and that happens more than we realize. A lot of the time physical problems have a deeper layer, because within the body, within the human being, there is not just one personality; there are several personalities. One of them is the normal day-to-day personality; the other ones, which are at a deeper layer, are the 'saboteur' and the 'savior'. They are two personalities.

For instance, if you do not want to do something, the body will often create a problem. You may say on a superficial level: "I want to do this." I have often heard people say to me: "Oh, I love yoga, I want to do it every day, I want to do it all the time, it is my passion." But then the next thing you know is that they have this problem, and then that problem, and then they have an appointment here, and a physical thing there, and so on and on. That is the 'saboteur' inside which does not really want to do yoga, so it sets into motion a whole series of little accidents, little problems, little things to prevent you from doing yoga. On the other hand, as the body is part of the quantum web, part of the whole of life, I think that the body also knows everything that is going on. It can hook on to the quantum web and feel the approaching future, and as it feels the approaching future, it can prevent it.

D O N A » Inside the body there is also the other half, the savior, let us say. That is why often, when you have a problem, through some chance meeting you get in touch with the right person who helps you solve or deal with this problem. Or there are strange instances when someone wants to get on an airplane but on the way to the airport gets into all kinds of little problems with the car and does not make it in time to the plane and misses it and the plane crashes. There are many of those instances. I think that the body knows much more than we realize and it can either sabotage your mental desires, your mental plans, or it can help you avoid problems. Once you understand those two entities below the surface it is a lot easier to deal with the totality of yourself. That is where you come to what you were saying just now.

D I A N A » I was saying the "yes, but..."

D O N A » The "yes, but...": That is the saboteur. I say: "Why don't you do this?" And the person answers: "Yes, but..." The 'yes' is OK, but the 'but' behind it means: "I do not want to know what you are saying, I do not want to deal with what you are saying, let us forget the whole thing." It is the denial, the retreat.

D I A N A » The 'savior' has to do with 'not-doing' and trusting our link to the universe?

D O N A » The 'saboteur' has to do with the deeper wishes that we have and they always win. The superficial wish is the weaker one and the deeper wish is the stronger one and that one always wins. The savior is another level, another layer, which has to do, as you say, with trust. From there you can move into the Taoist concept of wei-wu-wei. The Taoist concept of wei-wu-wei has a lot of different meanings. It means literally 'doing-without-doing'. It means that you get things done by no effort, by not applying any effort to get it done, but by, in a way, letting the universe 'work' for you. It also means that you trust that the universe will do that, so the wei-wu-wei is a trust thing. It is the trusting that you are a part of the universe, you are deeply embedded in the universe, you are an integral part of it, and so, basically, whatever you wish for is yours: it is your destiny. It was already meant to be yours. That is the whole idea of wei-wu-wei. If I want a certain thing, if I want to do yoga, then that is already my destiny, it is already prepared for me in some corner of the universe. All I have to do is acknowledge that link and it will come to me. The element of trust is that whatever I wish or whatever comes to me is already in the universe, is already part of me. It is the trust that I do not really have to 'work' for it, as it is already mine. As it is already mine I do not need to make a lot of effort to get it. On the contrary, anything I do to 'get' it will only make it harder. It is like putting pebbles in the way, or rocks in the way for it to come towards me. This is a very interesting concept and works both ways. It is the trust that everything is already yours, and it is also the trust that you do not have to work for things that hard. All you have to do is just make that link with the universe, with the pose. I apply it in the poses, so when I want to do a certain position like Full arm balance or any other position, I do not think: "Oh, I have to start from scratch and have to do a lot of work," but I think, that posture is already mine, the momentary posture is already mine. All I have to do is let it come to me and not me going there to grab it. So again it is getting out of the reward situation, just saying, "The reward is already mine." It is not in the future; it is already here. Acknowledging the present.

DIANA » You talked about chipping away and not adding. Is that the same concept?

DONA » The chipping away instead of the adding is the 'undoing'. You have the two concepts: 'doing' and 'undoing'. The 'doing' is going towards the reward and involves effort, time. 'Undoing' is not the opposite of 'doing', is not retreating. 'Undoing' is stopping to do, stopping the 'doing' and allowing the thing itself to manifest itself. In Florence in Italy, there is a museum with some statues made by Michelangelo. They are big marble rocks with people coming out of these rocks. They are half out of the rock and half still in the rock. A friend, Vanda Scaravelli, who used to take me there, said that Michelangelo said that these sculptures, these people were inside the marble and all he had to do was just chip the superfluous part away for these people to emerge out of the marble. The same thing with the piano; we used to play the piano and Vanda used to say to me: "The music is inside the piano; all you need to do is just allow it to come out of the piano, towards you; you are not putting the music into the piano. It is there and you help or allow it to come towards you out of the piano." It is the same thing with the postures. People impose a structure, a rule, a position on the body, and say: "This is what you have to do," completely ignoring the fact that the posture is inside the body. It is already there and so imposing an external posture or asana on the body is the 'doing', is the effort. It is the denial of the body and its inherent intelligence instead of saying to the body: "OK, the posture is there, let it come out," giving your loving consent. That is 'undoing'. You take the outer tensions away, the distractions, the harshness, the skin, everything... you just melt that out of the way, you move it to the side, and then the posture will come out of the body all by itself. In Taoist language that is called Jan-Tsu, 'the thing-that-does-itself'. There are many instances when that is exactly what you do. When you have a moment that you want to do something, if you are quiet enough and allow it to happen, it will happen by itself.

D I A N A » What do you do with all the painful and unjust situations? When you talk about this trust in the universe, what do you do about pain and injustice? People who feel that something in their life has been unjust, someone dying, or some violence. How to trust that link to the universe when there is pain involved?

D O N A » What is the word 'pain'? Nothing in the universe is 'painful'. 'Pain' is a human judgment put on a certain situation. It involves denial and the: "I do not like this, I hope it goes away" thought or feeling. It involves a retreating away from it, it involves a negative emotion going with it. The word 'pain' itself is an indication of denial, and it is a man-made indication of denial, because nothing in the universe has the label: "This is painful, and this is not painful." It is again a man-made thing in the same way that pleasure is a man-made thing; only pleasure is something that you want to gravitate towards because you think that that is nice, while pain is something you want to retreat from because you think it is not nice. Again you are back in the reward and the denial situation: that you want to get out of a certain situation and you want to get into the other situation; so again it means that you are never really standing still. You are not standing, you are always on the move, you are on the run, either backwards or forwards, but you are not standing still. When you stand still, even when something 'bad' happens, what we call bad - a death of somebody, or a pain - when that happens, if you do not deny it, do not run away from it, do not want to solve it, do not want to get rid of it; if you do not want to have a reward either, then you can just stay with it and the moment you stand still, stay with it, it changes. It changes because you take the emotional content that belongs to the word out of the situation. The emotional content belongs to the word; it does not belong to the situation. That is the interesting thing. It belongs to the word that we put on the situation.

The moment we take the word away we also take the emotional content away so we are left just with the experience, the situation. It is neither a 'bad' situation nor a 'good' one. It is just a situation, period. Then we can just be with it. You can experiment with it. In a moment that you are really angry for instance about something; if you stand still and look at it, almost splitting yourself: being angry on one level and on another level taking a couple steps backward and looking at yourself being angry, I can pretty well guarantee you that you will end up laughing, because the moment you retreat from it and look as an outsider at your anger it evaporates; it really evaporates.

DIANA » Is it like being in both worlds at the same time?

DONA » In a way that is being in both worlds at the same time, yeah. On the one hand you can play the game, and life is a game, a theater. Most people think that life is a serious game and that the game is for real. They do not realize that we ourselves are creating this game within this vast universe, we are doing it all ourselves. The tightrope situation comes in the picture when you can be in the middle. On the one hand play the game and play it wholeheartedly as if it really is important. On the other hand you are also on this side of the fence or the tightrope and you know that it is only a game, so you are sort of tongue-in-cheek or giggling-behind-your-hand about the whole thing. You can do both things at the same time.

DIANA » And that changes your experience in this world?

DONA » It changes the experience because you take the heavy and often self-righteous, emotional content away. As you take the label away you also take the emotion away so the whole thing softens. If, in your game, there is a problem and you call it a problem it becomes hard, it becomes a fixed thing. If you do not call it a problem then it is just a relationship. Therefore to be in the quantum mind is to see the world as a web of relationships, not as things-in-themselves. But if you take the game seriously then you take everything as a thing-in-itself. It is the same in the body: a knee is not a knee. To call something a knee is to limit it. A knee is, in reality, a meeting point of many relationships - between the hips, the legs, the ankles and the arches of the feet. They all meet in the knee. So the knee is the cross point of relationships. Therefore, if you have a knee problem, you cannot cure the knee problem as a thing-in-itself. You have to look at the whole range of relationships to see where there is an imbalance in these relationships. You cannot take a pill for a knee problem, that is very primitive. You have to look at the whole situation and then see: maybe the hip does not work enough, maybe the right knee is hurting because the left foot is not working enough. These are all relationships. It is the same thing in life: life is a network of relationships, a web of relationships. The whole quantum world, the whole universe, is a web of relationships - gravitational relationships, physical relationships. Therefore, if you take things as hard objects, as things-in-themselves, then they are detached from everything else. But if you take things as relationships then the structure is much looser and you can deal with it much easier.

DIANA » In yoga can the asana practice be taken as a showing of what happens in a larger context in life? In the sense that the asana practice can take us to the present moment, in which it does not matter so much that we are doing the pose, as much as our frame of mind during the pose?

DONA » The asana practice cannot take you to the present moment. Whenever we include time and a process-in-time we may go somewhere, and we most probably are going to arrive there, but wherever it is that we arrive at is always the same thing that we came from. To arrive at a completely new situation that has nothing to do with the old one you have to make that quantum leap and yoga in itself cannot do that. Yoga is only another system among so many systems. There are so many religions, so many philosophies, so many systems in the world and they all have a certain goal and some people may reach that goal; but as I said, the goal is always the same as the beginning, it is not different. Yoga is an all-round practice for the body to feel good, to be sensitive, to be healthy; but those things are by-products. We can use the practice of yoga to pay attention, but we cannot arrive at attention through the practice of yoga. Attention is a different thing. If you use yoga to arrive at attention that is again a process with attention as the goal, but if you use the practice of yoga as attention in itself then you do not allow that time process; the attention is there.

DIANA » That attention can happen while doing anything?

DONA » While doing anything; you do not need to do yoga. Yoga is fun to do. It feels good in the same way as it feels good to eat nice food. When you go to a restaurant you go there to eat nice food. There is no ulterior goal involved in it. You do not say, "I go to the restaurant to eat nice food in order to become enlightened or to get healthy." If you get healthy afterwards it is a by-product, it is a happy by-product. But it is not your main aim. The main aim is to have a pleasurable evening out. It is the same thing with yoga; it is like a little holiday. You are always busy with the office, the traffic jam, the cooking and the shopping and so yoga becomes like a little oasis in the middle of all the busy-ness where you can sit in your yoga room on your yoga mat and have a mini-holiday for an hour or two, like a little holiday on the beach.

DIANA » But you could have that holiday anywhere.

DONA » You could have that holiday anywhere, only it feels less good on the body to ride a bicycle to the office in the traffic smog than doing a couple of asanas. It is a question of physically feeling good, but that you can do of course everywhere. There is a difference though in moving the body in the yoga asanas or sitting in your office chair or behind your computer. That does not feel very good on the body because it is static, the blood circulation does not go. What the asanas do is simply stretching the body and whenever the body is stretched the fluids can flow easier. The fluids of the blood, the nervous energy, the electricity in the body, everything can flow more easily because you are stretching the body. This does not happen when you sit on a chair or in the car or behind the computer, you do not get that same effect. In that way there is a goal involved in the practice of yoga, but it is a very simple, not very important goal, not a very spiritual goal.

DIANA » So the practical goals are OK.

DONA » Practical goals are fine. We eat for the practical goal to survive. If we did not have the practical goal of survival we would not eat. Practical goals are OK, but if they become an emotional or a spiritual goal then you get into deep water, into a tangle. You get into a tangle because there is a reward. There is a corruption somewhere on the way. The moment you allow time and a reward you also allow corruption to set in.

DIANA » Is that where pain and frustration set in? When you want your reward and you do not get it?

DONA » You get the anger, the frustration and the pain because you want a reward and you are not getting it. The reward is always somewhere in the future and some people may get it and some may not. But even when you get it there is an old proverb which says: "Be careful what you ask for: you might even get it." Then what do you do? We may have a problem then, because our idea of the reward is in the mind, it is not in reality. As it is a thing only in the mind, when it manifests itself in reality it may be very different from what you visualized and then you have another problem to deal with.

DIANA » What do you think about the marketing in yoga, promising these practical goals? Do you think it is ethical?

DONA » There is a lot of discussion about the business side of yoga and of other systems, of marketing and whether it is ethical or not. These are again only man-made words. Business is only business, there is nothing wrong with it. Everything in life is done on business. I am very glad for business because when I am hungry I go to the shop and I buy bread. That is business; I give money and I get bread in return. I have no wish to go into the fields to sow grain to make my own bread. That is the good side of business. We should also remember that there is no business unless there is a demand for it, in the same way that there is no teacher unless there is a student, unless there is a demand for a teacher. There are always two things involved: if there is a business yoga-wise, if there is a marketing yoga-wise, it is because there is a demand for it. It is not only one side that is doing it; everybody is involved. The moment there is no longer a demand for business there won't be any.

DIANA » Our task is to be in our own space?

DONA » Of course; everybody is responsible for him- or herself; nobody is responsible for anybody else. Each human being is born complete. Each one of us has a complete link to the universe. Therefore it is my, and only my, responsibility to take care of my link. I cannot do this for another person. We are back to teaching: you cannot be a teacher. A teacher- student relationship is a phantom relationship, not a real one. In reality there are no teachers and no students. Life itself is the teacher and to go through a third person is an unreal situation. Life itself teaches us and each one of us has the responsibility to receive that teaching from the hands of life. Then you can exchange your experiences with other people, but you remain responsible for your own life, your own link.

DIANA » When you watch people's eyes you can see the depth behind their eyes. I think that that image can condense everything we are talking about here.

DONA » There is an old saying that the eyes are the windows of the soul. These old sayings really have a feeling for the situation. I think that the ears have a closer connection to the brain, to the electrical brain, to the thinking brain, to the continuous mind. But the eyes have a different connection inside, they are connected to the body, they are connected to the heart. Most of us have so many rules and regulations, do's and don'ts, so many words. We have the word 'pain', the word 'pleasure', the word 'ethical'; these words are like walls, dense areas in the eyes, so when you look into the eyes you hit these walls straight away, you hit straight away all these man-made constrictions and structures. We were talking about the house and opening all the windows of the house. The more you realize that these are all man-made things the more your horizon recedes. Each time the horizon goes a little bit further back so that you do not bang into a wall of do's and don'ts, and "this is right" and "this is wrong" when you look into the eyes of this person. The more windows are open and the more we are not bound by those man-made words and structures, the more our eyes show further and further spaces behind them which has to do with the connection between our inner being and the universe at large. The eyes open deeper and deeper into the star world.

7 Interview at Snake River

DIANA » How did you get originally interested in philosophy and religion?

DONA » How does one get interested in philosophy and religion? I think that when there is a lot of stress in your life, you will start to question, to ask about the why and the how. In the beginning of my life I went through a lot of very extreme situations. I was born in a Japanese concentration camp and after the war, when I was four years old, my family moved to a castle in Holland, where I lived for the next three years. Then we moved back to Indonesia, where my mother was born and raised. There was a civil war going on at that time in Indonesia. This moving back and forth between war and luxurious surroundings is very extreme and in a way stressful. I think that, by the time I got to the age of eight or ten, I had gone through all the different religions; the Thai religion, which is Buddhism, the Dutch religion, the Muslim religion. I had seen these different religions and I had seen that they all deal basically with human beings and their hopes and fears. When I was about ten, I began to read about Buddhism, but found it a little bit on the sad side. It is not a very happy religion and I got tired of it at a certain point. Then I moved on to Taoism. Taoism deals much more with nature, with the world as it is, with everything the way it is, and accepting that in a more easy and relaxed way than Buddhism or Christianity do. I got many good ideas out of Taoism, concepts that I later integrated in yoga like the concepts of wei-wu-wei, 'doing-without-doing' and Jan-Tsu, the 'act-which-does-itself' or the act that comes out of 'not-doing'. The other outcome of living through a lot of extremes and going through so many religions at such an early age and through so many countries is that it leaves you with a feeling that you are losing all the time. You are somewhere, you have friends, a house, a life, and then you lose it. You go somewhere else and you make new friends, a new life, and then again you lose it. And wars: in wartime everything is uncertain. Therefore I think I wanted to get deeper into not a general philosophy or a general religion, because I had seen those, but more into a personal feeling of re-mending that loss, of finding again a home, a place where I would belong. Specially because I lost a lot of people in that time, people, countries, and places and that leaves a feeling that you want to find something personal for yourself where you really feel the comfort zone, the personal comfort zone. I delved into various philosophies, mainly Taoism that I really enjoyed because it is simple and natural; it has to do with nature, being in natural surroundings, like here, which suited me very well. The other philosophy which I liked very much was Zen, but Zen is already much more intellectual, much more thinking about things, almost contrived in certain aspects.

My family came from a Theosophical background and my mother had been interested in Jiddhu Krishnamurti since the twenties, so it was natural that I drifted into that direction too. I met him when I was 18 years old. So, from all these sides I got different ideas, but most of them had to do with the direct, one-to-one link with the universe. Both Taoism and Krishnamurti and later on other people in my life accentuated that aspect, that each one of us is complete and can make that link, can establish that relationship which then makes you whole.

DIANA » So it was a personal seeking.

DONA » It was a very personal seeking. Of course the question always is: why, what is the cause of all this? One can make guesses, but I can only say that when I was eight or ten years old I was desperate for something in my life that would be there all the time, that would live inside my body, my heart, be my secret refuge. Probably that was a very big incentive; a very personal one also.

DIANA » You have talked about how you would practice in childhood wei-wu-wei when losing things, that you would tune yourself to find lost things. How could that happen so naturally and at such a young age?

DONA » I do not know. Some people have a gift for finding things. My mother had a tendency to accentuate certain aspects of the human being. For instance, everybody who knew me when I was two or three years old was convinced that I was going to be a dancer. I never became a dancer, but people saw in my body already the feeling for dance, for movement. Also, when I was very small, some people used me for curing their headaches, simple things like that. They used to put my hand on their head or on the hurting part of the body and the hurt used to go away. These things are natural but they get accentuated and developed by use and by acknowledgement from the surrounding people. There is a bodily sensitivity, a bodily knowledge and understanding, or maybe not even understanding but an intuitive feeling for the energy body inside, because it is the energy body which cures other people and which finds things, not the physical body. That sensitivity can be developed, in fact I did some work on that.

DIANA » Do you think that we all come with a certain amount of awareness of the energy body and then develop that, or there are different types of people with different kinds of awareness?

DONA » I think that all children have it and that it depends on the surroundings whether that awareness is stifled and put under cover or whether the child is encouraged to pay attention to it and to develop it. You must be lucky to have surroundings to do that for you, to help you to not stifle it and put it away but to keep it and bring it out.

DIANA » Do you think that as a girl they did not interfere with your natural...

DONA » On the contrary, I was helped a lot, but you must remember that we were in a post-war situation. When my family came out of the camps everybody was dispersed. It was not that you went home and had your aunt and your uncle and everybody. It was a family under stress so anything that would be good and nice would be encouraged and helped.

DIANA » When did yoga start in your life?

DONA » Yoga was a natural development, because apart from being passionately interested in finding this link with the universe, finding reality, finding my personal fulfillment with that, I was also very sportive. I liked sports and did a lot of horse riding and other sports. I was drifting from one to the next just to find out a way of getting the body as much as possible moving in all directions, which most sports do not do. I played a lot of tennis, for instance, but tennis is always with one arm and shoulder. Ping-pong was the same way.

Horse riding was very nice and I learned a lot from horse riding. My horse-riding teacher was my first 'guru'; I worshipped that man. But in all those sports I was looking for something that would exercise the whole body in a really nice way and at the same time help it to be as sensitive and as open to the life force as possible so that the body would not bounce the force off, let us say, by harshness and insensitivity, but would receive reality, the life force, harmoniously and with ease.

DIANA » Do you think the element of luck has something to do with finding those teachers?

DONA » There is a large element of luck in it. But again, if you believe in the quantum web and that everything is a unified whole, then how much do you look for luck and therefore luck comes to you, or how much does luck come to you and you are fast and alert enough to catch it? Which one comes first, the hen or the egg? I was lucky in my life; I had extraordinary people in my life, people who were amazing. Each one of them brought out something in me and helped me to see the world in a new way. I mentioned the main names: Jiddhu Krishnamurti who was my first real eye opener, and yoga-wise B.K.S. Iyengar from India who taught me all the asanas, the practical aspect of yoga. Then I met Vanda Scaravelli when I was quite young, in the mid sixties. She was also an eye-opener because she was a woman. I had got into a very close relationship with her through the piano and through living in her house for a while. It was a very intense exchange with her.

DIANA » Who was she?

DONA » Vanda Scaravelli was one of the richest Countesses, a member of an important Jewish family, in Florence. She was a concert pianist but when she married her husband she gave up her career to be with her husband. He was a famous philosopher and writer. When she married him she still had a lot of contact with many artists, pianists, and painters. Anybody in that time who was important and had a name came to Vanda Scaravelli's house. She was also a very good friend of Krishnamurti, almost like a sister to him in a certain way. So she had a lot of qualities that were eye openers. We developed a relationship, which was intense.

DIANA » Why was she an eye-opener? What did you learn from her?

DONA » The way she was. As we said before, most people, when you look into their eyes, there is a shallowness, a hardness or wall behind the eyes that stops you. She was one of those very few people who you would look into the eyes and felt like you could go endlessly on and on and on and on. There was such a depth and such a length and such a distance in the eyes. Which was, of course, also in Krishnamurti's eyes. That has to do with what you are, the internal spirituality. I played a lot of piano with her and through the piano she taught me about yoga, which is very interesting. She used to say that the music is already in the piano and all you have to do is not impose on the piano, but just pull the music out of the piano. In the same way you pull the posture out of the body; the posture is in the body and all you do is pull it out. Apart from that she was just a very laughing personality. It was very light to be around her, which was extremely pleasant. We had a lot of fun together apart from the serious aspect.

DIANA » Was she also an Iyengar student?

DONA » She studied with Iyengar for a while. She was also very independent; independent on the one hand and generous on the other hand. She studied with him and then she wanted to do her own thing, but she always gave him credit and talked about him in a very generous way.

DIANA » She learned from Iyengar and then developed her own...

DONA » She learned the postures from Iyengar when she was 55 years old, but she was small, thin, and quite supple, so that age was not a big problem for her. But then she wanted to work on this energy thing. For her it was important to not only move the body, but to move the inner energy. She worked a lot with gravity and with breathing. She was very much into breathing. She gave me a lot of input.

DIANA » Why was Iyengar such a good teacher as far as the asanas go?

DONA » To learn the asanas, to learn anything, not only yoga, you need to have a symbiosis of two people, a keen teacher and a keen student. One person alone cannot do it. I went to India the first time in 1964 and in 1969 for the second time. Iyengar hardly spoke English, he was really very Indian; a little wild, a lot of flying energy. In 1964 I was about twenty-two years old, also with a lot of flying energy. So between these two personalities we clashed and at the same time we matched very well. We were both a little bit wild, flying, a lot of energy, a lot of excitement. On the one hand it was bad because we clashed all the time; but on the other hand we understood each other very well. He taught me everything in six months, all the asanas in six months. Then of course it took me forty years to smooth it all out, to make the movements, the exercises look the way they look now. Back then it was like two fireballs coming together.

KARINA» How old was Vanda when you met her?

DONA » I met her somewhere in 1965 or 1966 for the first time in Krishnamurti's house. Then I lost sight of her, but met her again in 1971 when I stayed with her in Italy.

DIANA » Tell me more about when you started practicing yoga. You came back from India and...

DONA » I went to India in 1964 for the first time to practice yoga with Iyengar. I had met him in Krishnamurti's house and I had told Krishnamurti that I wanted to become a teacher of yoga, so he said: "Well, in that case, you should go to the best which is Iyengar." So I went to Iyengar.

DIANA » When you started practicing yoga, did you almost immediately start teaching?

DONA » No, before meeting Iyengar I practiced yoga in Holland. I was studying at the time Sanskrit, but then I thought that I did not want to waste time. I wanted to do yoga, therefore I decided to go to India to study to become a teacher so that I could practice and teach yoga at the same time.

DIANA » Do you think teaching what you know from the asanas is an important part of doing yoga?

DONA » Teaching is an important part of anything because in teaching you have to formulate what you know. Practice will bring you knowledge; teaching never brings you knowledge. Practice will bring you knowledge, but then you have to formulate that knowledge and bring it out to other people by teaching.

DIANA » Why do you feel the need to do that?

DONA » There is no need for teaching yoga. I just like doing it, that is all.

DIANA » Do you have fun?

DONA » It can be a lot of fun and it can be also difficult at times. When you have a student who is really keen and eager and understands your teaching it can be a lot of fun.

DIANA » Now you travel around the world giving courses?

DONA » I do a lot of traveling and teaching everywhere.

DIANA » Do you like that?

DONA » Yes.

DIANA » Your schedule is amazing. How do you put up with it? How can you keep on doing it year after year, one week here, one week there?

DONA » I have a very busy schedule and the traveling is hard. It is hard on the body and sometimes it is difficult, but as I said, one has to always apply things in daily life. I have learned how to replenish myself again by the quantum leap, by plugging into the universe, relaxing. I know how to do that and that takes me out of my fatigue quite fast.

DIANA » I wanted to ask you what different stages in your yoga practice you can identify? Like turning points that changed the way you practiced or thought about yoga.

DONA » I think those turning points have to do with the people whom I met. Iyengar was definitely a turning point in my perception of yoga. He taught me a very vigorous type of yoga, while before it was all very soft and easy. He brought me to a vigorous part of yoga, and Vanda brought me to a more energetic part of yoga, a more - quote/unquote - feminine view on yoga. Those were probably the main turning points in my life.

DIANA » What do you mean with feminine and masculine?

DONA » Iyengar is a man. A female can learn from a man, but certain things you have to learn from another female. The softness, the smoothness, the roundness of the movement you can learn better from another woman.

DIANA » Why do you think that there are more women practicing yoga than men?

DONA » In the first place there are more women than men in the world. Almost everywhere you look you see women outnumbering men. Men also look more for tough sports when they are young, or they are shy or just too busy making a career. In general, women have more time to do side things, and yoga is definitely for most people a side thing.

DIANA » Do you think many people are attracted to yoga when they are older?

DONA » Not particularly. People do yoga in all ranges of age. It is not something for young people or old people only.

DIANA » I wanted to ask you about teachers. You mentioned other inspirations from, for example, the Fairbanks movies. That was not someone you met directly. Do you think that learning from someone directly is more powerful than learning through a film, for example?

DONA » I do not think so. When you are ready for a certain input it does not matter where that input comes from. This is the whole idea: it can come from a photograph, from a movie, from an animal. If you are ready for something new, for a particular thing, then when that comes you can pick it up. It can be from a living person, from a dead person, from a movie star, from an animal, from a dancer, anything.

124 **Eyes of Innocence**
Dona Holleman

8   Interview at String Lake

DIANA » Can you tell us the juggler story?

DONA » This is a famous story from the Middle Ages about a young man who was a little dumb, a little backward. He lived in the country and could not read or write. The only thing he could do was juggle. He worked in a circus, that is how he earned his money but he was not good for anything else. At a certain point he was put in a monastery where he became a servant. He had to do all kinds of menial jobs, cleaning the kitchen, sweeping the floors, things like that, while the other monks were reading, writing, and praying. Because he was a little dumb they always teased him, making fun of him. He got more and more miserable, more and more upset, till finally he could take it no longer. He could not do anything, he had nothing to give, no money, no wealth, the only thing he could do was juggle. So he went to the chapel of the Madonna, 'La Notre Dame'; that is why he is called 'Le jongleur de Notre Dame', stood in front of the Madonna statue and began to do the only thing he could do: juggle, as an offering to her, as a way of making contact, as a way of giving all that he had. The juggling was all he had and he gave it to her. The other monks saw him disappear in the chapel. They thought that was strange and followed him. When they came into the chapel they saw him juggling in front of the statue of the Madonna and they got very upset as they thought it was a profane thing to do. They wanted to stop him, tell him to get out of there, but at that moment the statue of the Madonna came down from the altar, with her hand took the corner of her mantle and began to wipe the face of the juggler, wipe his tears and his sweat off his face, while the monks looked on, amazed.

The story is very symbolic. It is a sweet and symbolic story in the sense that the monks were all very intellectual, very proud; they had a lot of achievement, but they did not have a heart. The juggler could neither read or write, he could not do anything at all, but he just loved the Madonna and so he offered her what he could, which was his juggling: that was all he had. He offered it to her with his full heart, with his full love and affection, crying and sweating. He was the one that she came down for to protect, to help, and to console while the other monks were left out.

DIANA » So you would say that it does not matter what it is that we do, as long as we do it to the best of our ability?

DONA » It does not matter what you do as long as it is the best of yourself, and as long as it is done without the reward in mind.

Whatever you do, if you do it with the reward in mind it is corrupt, it is not a true gift. The true gift is when you give of yourself, whatever you have, without expecting anything in return, with full affection, full gratitude for whatever has come to you in life.

DIANA » In a way it is a paradox: the fact that he did not expect a reward, in this case from the Madonna, but is the one to get it.

DONA » Exactly, because the reward comes when you do not expect it. When you work in order to achieve something then you may achieve that, but it is never a true thing, it is never the 'Madonna', let us say it that way. The real thing comes when you do whatever you can and then, on the principle of wei-wu-wei, let go of whatever you did, not waiting to get the fruit of your action. Then, whatever comes to you, you will have a real gratitude for it and moreover it will be something real, because you have not created it with your expectations.

DIANA » How can you relate this story to the practice of the asanas?

DONA » When we practice the positions of yoga with a certain aim in mind we may get results, but they are always within the man-made structure. Whatever man-made path you choose to get a result the result is bound to be man-made; that is because of the time and the language thing. If you practice the asanas without having any expectations of a reward, of a goal, of a future, then you are in the asana, in the practice, and therefore there is great beauty, just the body flowering. It is the body flowering, but not flowering in order to... It is just flowering.

DIANA » You talk about doing something for the sake of perfection.

DONA » That is the perfection. The perfection is when you do something without looking over the horizon, when you are completely in the moment. Perfection is not that you do something technically perfect; it does not have to be technically perfect. Perfection is when your mind and your heart fill the body completely in the pose, in the asana, in whatever you do.

DIANA » What happened when you heard this story? When did you hear it and what happened?

D O N A » Oh, I do not remember, these stories come from my teenage time, a long time ago. But because they are so poignant, because they are so clear and simple, they are easy to remember.

D I A N A » Do you think a story like this can change the way you perceive?

D O N A » Again, you are back at the same point. Things can only change you if you are ready for the change. If somebody is not ready for that particular change you can use a sledgehammer and yet nothing will happen. But if somebody is ready for a particular change, then even a drop of water on the lake can do the trick of changing.

D I A N A » The doing something for the sake of perfection. Can this relate to art?

D O N A » Of course, art is exactly the same as yoga. Art is the art of living. Art is looking at life through your particular eyes; then you interpret, but before you interpret you have to see; and in order to see you have to be very quiet, very inward.

D I A N A » Can you tell us about your ideas about the depth of people's eyes?

D O N A » Vanda used to say that when you walk in the street you see so many people passing by. She used to give me an exercise. She used to say: "Find out how many times on a day when people walk by you want to turn around and have a second look at the person." It does not happen very often that you want to have a second look because something is striking you about that person. What is striking is usually the eyes, because the eyes are the windows of the inner being. They are the gateway between the inner being and the outer world. Most people are limited in their inner being, limited in their link with life, the universe, so when you look into their eyes you get stopped straight away. You look into the eyes and there is something that stops you right behind the eyes, there is not a great depth. But sometimes it happens that you walk in the street, or you meet somebody, and you look into the eyes and it is again like a vortex, but this time a good vortex, a positive vortex, which pulls you in, and you can go very far in, over lakes, and fields, and woods; a very great distance because that inner being behind the eyes has a great inner distance.

DIANA » When you talk about doing one's own personal thing to the best of one's ability, do you think each one of us has a special personal thing that is our task?

DONA » Yeah. I think that each one of us, when we are born, has a special talent, a special thing that we have to do. As far as human happiness goes I think you can get as close as possible to it if you do what you are good at and what you like doing. Most people are trapped within a situation where they have to do something for money or for another reason; something that is not really their thing, their inner vibration, their inner vision, and which does not fit them. So there is no real joy in what they are doing. I remember a phrase from Henry David Thoreau where he says that most people lead lives of quiet desperation. That is another poignant phrase and, I think, very true in that most people exist without really living totally. You live totally when you fill your day with what you are good at and which you love doing which is the same thing.

DIANA » So the juggler was accepting his talent and that is why he could be there in full awareness.

DONA » Yeah, the juggler brought his talent, his expertise to the highest authority he could find which was - in his case - the Madonna. He offered it to the highest authority as a true gift, as a true devotion, a dedication.

DIANA » And that was enough?

DONA » That was enough; he did not have to do anything else. There was no point in him learning to read or write, that was something the other monks could do. But they could not juggle, and certainly not in front of the Madonna. That was his thing, and she accepted that, it was enough what he did.

DIANA » There is a certain innocence?

DONA » Innocence; it is innocence, yeah.

DIANA » In opening oneself and giving the best...

DONA » Giving the best. Innocence is giving the best that you can, the best you are capable of and giving it freely, gratuitous. Giving it freely in the sense of not giving it with an ulterior motive of wanting something back. What the story tries to say is that the monks were clever and learned and were reading and writing because they expected a certain reward. They expected paradise, they expected God to come down and reward them. But the juggler was so humble, in his own eyes nothing. He did not expect anything and so he just brought what he had.

DIANA » But that is not small...

DONA » That is not small. He felt small in the sense that the monks were teasing him all the time. But the Madonna did not think he was small because she came down for him. She did not come down for the other monks.

DIANA » Is that what we could call the vertical experience?

DONA » This is an allegorical story, a medieval story. It definitely has to do with the vertical experience, with reaching out vertically into the universal force.

DIANA » Why do you call it vertical?

DONA » Because the horizontal exchange is what we do as human beings. In the man-made world you only have horizontal exchanges - everything is based on give and take. People never do anything without expecting something back. It is a market. Human life is a market place: I give you bananas and you give me apples, and if you do not give me apples then I get upset. There is always an energy exchange between human beings. I call the other one vertical, because you do not deal with other people, with teachers or students. You deal with the universe. That is on a vertical line, you tap directly into the energy of the cosmos, not into the energy of other people. What people usually do when they feel inadequate, empty, miserable is try to overcome that by taking energy from other people. In a way we are all the time on the stealing path. We try to steal energy and attention from others either by the way we behave or by being sick or by being aggressive or by other ways. We try to get people's attention and attention stands for energy in this case. We try to fill up our own energy by 'stealing' from other people, by hook or by crook. That is the horizontal level. In the vertical level you leave everybody alone. You leave this world alone and you plug directly into the higher force, the universal force, the non-human force.

DIANA » How do we know which one is that special talent?

DONA » That each one has? There is no answer to that. Each one has to find that for himself. It is when you do it and you really feel that it is you. Nobody else can tell you what that is. It is a mistake that people go to gurus or teachers or to some other person and ask them: "What should I do?" It is a mistake. Only you can know what is your thing, what is your deepest talent.

DIANA » What about somebody who has many talents?

DONA » Then that is your talent, to have many talents, to explore those talents to the maximum. To receive them and to use them to the maximum. To groom them.

DIANA » Do you think happiness has to do with accepting that?

DONA » Sure, it has to do with accepting your particular being, your particular life substance, your particular life essence.

DIANA » Do you want to add anything?

KARINA » What about talent and responsibility?

DONA » What do you mean with talent and responsibility?

KARINA » The more talent you have, the more responsibility you have towards yourself, towards the universe?

DONA » And then what?

KARINA » And then what if you have a talent and you do not develop it?

DANIEL » You are just simply stupid.

DONA » OK, we can do that. You want to do the responsibility thing?

DIANA » Dona, you were going to tell us the relationship between talent and responsibility.

DONA » Between talent and responsibility. When you have a talent it is your responsibility to develop that. The word responsibility sounds sometimes a little bit daunting, a little bit grim. If you really accept your talent, that which you are good at, and you are willing to risk for that, then it is also very joyful, not only responsible. It is a joyful thing, because you are good at it; it is parallel to your inner being. While if you do something else which is not parallel to your inner being, sooner or later you are going to clash. So the responsibility is there, but it is a willing responsibility, a joyful responsibility, not a grim one.

DIANA » The same with discipline, right?

DONA » The same with discipline. If you do not like what you are doing then you have to discipline yourself; but if you like what you are doing, you do not have to discipline yourself, because you like doing it, you are good at it. When you go to a nice restaurant you do not have to discipline yourself to eat, you just sit down and eat. But if you do not like the food, you have to force yourself. Forcing, discipline, and responsibility are always slightly on the harsh side; while if you accept your talent and really go with it, roll with it, then it is a liberating experience.

DIANA » What about inertia? When you are in the pleasure thing and do not really listen to your body? How to get out of that?

DONA » Inertia is the opposite of being interested, so again you have to force yourself, you have to discipline yourself, you have to do all those things from the outside; but if you are interested, if you are really inside whatever it is you are doing, then inertia is not there. It is only there when you are not really interested, not really with it that there is inertia.

JOSH » You were talking about Taoism, how you were interested in it for a while and took a lot from it. I want to know what eventually led you away from it?

DONA » I was interested in many philosophies. I went through them, took what I wanted, and then left them to go somewhere else. I have been calling those systems also vortexes. I always say that you should be like a pirate: go into the ship, get the gold, and get out of it again, not stay in there. Sink the ship after you got what you were looking for. I took all the gold I could get out of Taoism, out of Buddhism, but I did not stay in them. If you stay in them and do not sink the ship straight away, inertia starts setting in and then it becomes a trap, a vortex. Just take what you can, use it, and then move on. You have to keep moving. This is the Greek saying: pantha rei, everything is in flux, everything is moving, like the river. You put your boat in the water and it keeps moving because there is a current. If you do not stay in the current, if you hang on to a rock in the current, then you get stuck. So I take what I can... from a movie, a book, a philosophy; I go in there, look around to see what I might need, and then I come out again.

9 Interview sitting on a tree with Snake River as background

DONA » "We never look with eyes of innocence, we always look through our hopes, fears, thoughts and experiences. These form a wall in front of our eyes; a troubling like the ripples on a lake that distort our reflection of reality. Seldom do we look into the eyes of our fellow men and women, and when we do, we find ourselves stopped by this wall; but on a rare occasion we may meet someone and look into the eyes, and to our surprise do not find ourselves stopped, but rather invited to enter into endless rolling fields and routes, vistas of innocent beauty."

DIANA » Tell me about the eyes and the depth.

DONA » The eyes are the windows of the interior. With most of us, when we look through our own eyes or look into other people's eyes, there is a lot of material in them which is very dense - the past, the present, the future, thoughts, emotions, experiences. But sometimes somebody can be out of that frame and therefore the eyes have a very different clarity. They have a clarity where you can go inside the eyes and you do not get hit by the experiences and by the past of that person, by the thoughts of that person.

DIANA » So instead of seeing a wall you see a depth?

DONA » Yes, they are like a tunnel that opens out into endless vistas. There is a long range in there which is not visible in most people, because their range of thought and experience is so short, their vision is literally very short. That long vision means that the person who has that long vision thinks through a lot of different dimensions, let us say.

DIANA » It does not stop you like a wall?

DONA » It does not stop you like a wall. It does not hit you when you look in there.

DIANA » Does that affect the way we relate to people?

DONA » I am sure it affects the way we relate to people. In the first place we never look at each other and if we do, there is straight away a fear, a mutual fear, a rejection, a hiding; people hide inside because there are a lot of things to hide. While if a person is really innocent there is nothing to hide. Their eyes are like the eyes of a baby, clear, and you can go in there and they are like a whirlpool that draws you in. Grown ups do not have that kind of inviting look in their eyes. The key word in all this is 'judgment'. When we look at life, at the world, as it comes into our eyes, we judge and the judgment is what we throw back at what we are seeing and hearing. It is this judgment, which is the wall. But if we can receive what comes from outside and not have a reaction, not judge, not throw the ball back, then we only receive and so what we receive is unclouded by our hopes, fears, thoughts, emotions and experiences. Therefore what we receive is a clear reflection.

DIANA » Who do you know who had those eyes?

DONA » Vanda Scaravelli had them, and certainly Krishnamurti. I have met a few people like that in life, but very few.

DIANA » You watched them and it pulled you?

DONA » No, they were just very clear eyes, very deep eyes.

JOSH » What role do you think romantic attraction has when looking into someone's eyes?

DONA » Romantic attraction has to do with other things, not with the clear reflection, because romance has to do with emotional things, while what we are talking about here has nothing to do with either thoughts or emotions. That is what I am saying; usually, when we see something we have a reaction. I react with my hopes, like in the romance, or my fears, or my emotions, my past, my history. On the other hand what we are talking about now is just looking at the world and not stopping it with our judgment or with our past. It is again that quantum leap where we do not allow the past, the present, or the future to interfere but we only receive like the lake receives the reflection. But if there is a wind, a disturbance, then there are ripples that make the reflection unclear. So it is not emotional, it is not thought: it is a clear reflection that is totally outside psychological time.

DIANA » Do you think that that is the main idea of everything that we have talked about?

DONA » It is the main idea of everything we have talked about. When you see a tree, a mountain, an animal, or another person and do not straight away split that vision into good and bad with your judgment; because judgment always splits things. When you do not do that but just allow the tree, or the sky to come to you without doing anything back to it then you enter into a different relationship with it. That relationship, we have talked already about it before, does not go through the brain but through the body, through the atoms of the body, through the heart. Not the emotional heart, but a different heart. The only word you can put on it is that you enter into a relationship of loving; not loving as a romance, but loving in an unconditional way. Romance is always conditional: if you do not love me back I will hate you. But the trees will not love you back in that same way. It is not a question of giving and taking, but the moment you enter into that relationship of seeing and receiving the tree, the sky, the mountains, there is that feeling of affinity, that feeling of belonging, which you can only describe as a feeling of love. The trees will love you back - but not because you want it.

DIANA » Is that love our link to the universe? Maybe that heart, that love we feel for the world is recognizing that link that we all have for the universe?

DONA » We all have that link with the universe, we are part of the universe, we are part of the world, we are part of everything. When we allow the body and ourselves to feel that, to acknowledge that, to live that, then you do have a different relationship; because that relationship does not go through our judgments, our thoughts, our thinking process, but it goes through a different part of us, through a different section of us, through the heart.

DIANA » The other day I heard you say that you thought that this movie was about freedom. What kind of freedom?

DONA » Freedom is an over-used word. Most people think that freedom implies that you are free to do what you want. That is not what freedom is about, not in this context. Freedom is that you acknowledge that one-to-one link to the universe and that you take full responsibility for that. You take full relationship and you live it fully, and you take care of your own link. That is freedom. You do not have to give an account to anybody - a guru, a teacher, a saint, or a religion. You are fully responsibility for yourself and for your relationship.

DIANA » Have you lived your life like that?

DONA » Yeah. This whole thing of being in the world and living a direct relationship with the universe was with me long before I did yoga. Yoga is only a part of it; a small part, not the main thing.

DIANA » What is the main thing?

DONA » The main thing is this relationship and the feeling of your responsibility and your love. Let us say it this way, that everything we do - including yoga, including any other philosophy or practice - is only a fragment. What is important and what has been the main thing in my life is the whole. To be with the whole, not to be only with a fragment of it, a part of it. Yoga is good: it is healthy, fun, a good tool. But if you think that the tool is the whole thing then I think you are on the wrong track because you get lost in the tool and you lose all this.

DIANA » So the tool can be a wall...

DONA » The tool can definitely be a very big wall in front of people's eyes and it often is, so they lose the beauty of everything. And not only the beauty of everything, but also the ugliness of everything, because beauty and ugliness are again only words. Again there is the division between this-is-good, that-is-not good; the Cowboy Bar is a bad place and the mountain is a good place; in this way you lose both. That is also the idea of the tightrope, that you are always in everything, that everything is the same.

CHRIS » A summersault is as spiritual as yoga?

DONA » Definitely. Things are only things; what makes them spiritual or not spiritual is you. If you are not spiritual you can do ten hours of meditation a day, but if your mind is stuck you are not doing anything. If your mind is free, if you are full of love, full of the world, then, whatever you do, it is spiritual. It is not the thing that makes it spiritual; it is the eyes with which you look at the things.

DIANA » Those are the eyes of innocence?

DONA » Exactly. The eyes of innocence that do not judge. If you say summersaults and juggling are not spiritual and yoga is spiritual, then the question is: Who decides that? And why? And based on what? What is your criterion? What is your criterion based on? You end up in a bog of questions. As we go through life we always have a little stick in front of us. This stick is the - quote/unquote - 'truth', it is the ideal. The stick says: "This thing here is good." Then, whatever comes in our way, we put it next to the stick and we say: "Does it look the same? No, it does not look the same, so it must be bad." Then, something else comes along, we put it next to the stick, comparing it to the stick, and we say: "Yeah, it looks more or less the same." So we say: "That is good," forgetting that the stick in front of our eyes is only a stick put there by society, culture, religion, and our own past. In reality there is no stick, in reality the stick is us. If we do not have the stick, then nothing is good and nothing is bad, nothing is ugly and nothing is beautiful. It just is.

DIANA » Then we have no safety zone?

DONA » No safety zone whatsoever. The stick is the safety zone, because we 'know' what is good, we 'know' what is spiritual. We forget that the stick is a phantom. As long as we have the stick that says: "This is spiritual," we can put the juggling next to it. We say: "No, the juggling does not look the same as the stick, so juggling is not spiritual." We go to the church and put a candle for the Madonna: "Yeah, that looks more or less the same as the stick. So that is spiritual." We are ruled by the phantom stick.

DIANA » Is it not scary not to have that?

DONA » Of course it is scary, everything is scary. The safety zone is a camouflage for scariness. But because you have your safety zone, or think that you have one, that does not mean that you are not at the risk of your life every second of your life. The safety zone is another phantom; it just fools you. Freedom is when you take the fooling part away and say: "OK, I can die any second, I can get lost any second." Then you may realize that you cannot get lost, there is no way you can fall off the earth, you cannot get lost out of the universe. The safety zone is a fool's paradise. In this universe there is no safety zone, and that absolute realization is your safety zone.

DIANA » Can you say that again, please?

D O N A » In this universe there is absolutely no safety zone. Any safety zone you create - whether it is yoga, or religion, or your husband, or your family, or your house - is a fool's paradise.

D I A N A » So we must face that?

D O N A » Exactly. And take it for what it is: a fool's paradise. It does not mean you cannot have a house. It does not mean you have to live in the bush. You can still have a house, but you know at the same time that your house can fall down in an earthquake, your house can burn down, it can disappear. Everything is insecure. This is the whole thing, what the Greeks used to say: panta rei: everything is flowing. There is no guarantee whatsoever of a continuation of this moment. Any guarantee that you give, or think that you have, is a fool's paradise.

D I A N A » Do you think the awareness of death has something to do with that?

D O N A » Definitely. The fool's paradise, the safety zone, is that you think: "Other people die, I won't die." That is your safety zone. But of course, we also die. We create all these fool's paradises, and then we live in them; and then, when the fool's paradise falls apart, we are upset. We are lost; we go neurotic, because our little raft has sunk. And then, instead of taking that as a sign that we have to swim, we build another raft, we look for another raft. People lose faith in Christianity and then they go to Buddhism. That is not a solution; you just make a sidestep instead of going forward into the abyss. People just take sidesteps: this does not work anymore so I go sideways, then again, this does not work anymore, so I go sideways. I go sideways instead of jumping into the unknown.

D I A N A » Do you think it is similar to why the West is looking to Eastern philosophy?

D O N A » Of course. The West looks for Eastern philosophy, the East comes to the West for beautiful cars - the grass is always greener over the hill. Whatever the other cat is eating is much tastier than what you have, even though it comes out of the same tin. The West goes to the East. Why? As if we do not have spirituality here. Why would India or China only have spirituality? Or Japan? We have the same sky, we have the same stars, we have the same grass, we have everything the same; we have the same skin, we have the same body. What is wrong? Why do we have to look somewhere else? Everything is right here. This tree is the most spiritual thing you can come upon in life, the most beautiful, the most spiritual thing. Why do you have to go China to find one?

CHRIS» Why not go to China?

DONA» Go to China, by all means, but just go and have a dip in the Yang-Tse river, have fun, climb the wall; but do not go there to find God, Life. God is here, right here in front of our feet. Saves you a couple of thousand bucks not going there. Unless you want to go there. I want to go to Japan, but not to find God, or something spiritual. I can be right here and get it here; this is my safety zone.

JOSH» You said God. I asked you about God earlier and you laughed at me.

DONA» No, I do not laugh. The word God is a horrible word. It is also a man-made word. I say the universal force, the universe, life, the world. What does God mean? If you say God, then somebody else will say Allah, and then you have war, because my Allah is better than your God, or your Jehovah, and who else do we have? How many Gods do we have in the world? It is an abused word, so I prefer to say the universe, life, the life force, the universal force.

DIANA» I have heard you talk about the two worlds, and at some point I remember Josh asking if you were assigning a value judgment to one world or the other, like the quantum world over our everyday or man-made world. Do you think that is true, that one is more valuable than the other?

DONA» There really are not two worlds, this is the whole thing. There is only one world, but we have two ways of looking at it. One way is 'looking', and one way is 'seeing'. When we 'look' at the world we look with the past, the future, the present, which means that we look through that veil or that wall which is necessary, because we have to live in this world, we need to apply judgments all the time. But we can switch the eyes. We can 'see'.

DIANA » You were saying about 'seeing' and 'looking'?

DONA » The world is the same. It depends on whether we 'look' or whether we 'see'. The world is the same, this quantum world, this thing out there. When we 'look' at it we make that structure which serves to live in it. We need to structure, and the structure is our judgment, is the words that we apply. We forget however that it is only a small portion of what is out there, it is a man-made structure. This is what I was saying: one building is spiritual, another one is not. That is a man-made structure, because a building is only a building. The other way is when we 'see', and that is the innocent way, because we do not harm things. When we 'look', we harm things, we alter them by the way we look at them, while if you make that quantum leap and you are out of the usual judgment situation, then what you 'see' is the real thing, but you cannot describe it, because the real thing is beyond description. Any description you give brings it again back into the human frame. The fool's paradise that we live in is that we think that by giving a word to a thing we know what it is. That is not true at all. We will never know the world, but we create a phantom safety zone where we think that we know what a tree is. We will never really know it; there is no way we can know it.

JOSH » That just puts me in mind again of physics... of light being either a particle or a wave, and neither or both, depending on how we look at or try to measure it.

DONA » There is the world out there; you have that link, but you can never put it into words, into a description, because the moment you describe it you are back in the past, present and future - psychological time - and therefore in a time and space situation. In physics you have the particle and the wave but neither of them is the real thing; the real thing is probably something else behind it. The world is something, and we perceive it through our senses. The senses bring the sounds, the smells and the colors into our nervous system, into our mind and out of that input we construct the world and then we get trapped in it. It is again the vortex in our brain; we get trapped in that world. We gradually withdraw from the outside and look only at the inner world: the cave of Plato, with people looking at the shadows on the inner wall while outside is the sun and the beauty.

DIANA » I heard you mention we should have equal love for both our ways of perceiving the world.

DONA » Equal love for everything, not only for both ways of perceiving. We should understand that we live in a man-made world and not condemn that, because sometimes people say: "Oh, this world is bad. It is a world full of sorrow, a bad world." I think that that is missing the point, missing the acknowledgement that it is only half the truth, half the picture. We should understand the man-made world with all the things that we created in it, but you understand also that it is only a mirage, a fata morgana, and not condemn it. Not to say that it is bad; not to condemn it, but not to get sucked into it either. And not to say: "Oh, we have to get to Nirvana. Nirvana is going to be eternal bliss." Because you deny either the one or the other. So not to deny either, but to live in the man-made world and to live with full gusto. And at the same time also be able to switch in the sense that for a moment you put the man-made world on hold and dip into the other world where you do not judge and create things, but where you only observe and be part of everything.

DIANA » Do you think we have to make the best of our being human beings on earth by living with that gusto.

DONA » Yeah. What we forget is that each human being is responsible. By what you are, what you think, and what you feel you are responsible for what happens in the world. If you say: "Human beings are bad," you are only contributing to that, you are helping human beings to be 'bad'. If you say: "Animals are bad," you are contributing to that. We make this world but we make it all together.

It is not that other people make the world and I am suffering. We all make it together and we make it together by the way we create this fata morgana. The more positive you are the more you are of help in creating a brighter fata morgana.

KARINA» So you would not be against the thought that cataclysms maybe the result of negativity, like earthquakes, or tornados?

DONA» I think that if you really go into this feeling of the one web, the one net, the one jelly - I like to think of it as a jelly - and that we are all bubbles in the jelly - then it is likely that the more negativity there is the more the jelly will vibrate. Thus, by the way you are, the inner peace you have, the inner distance you have you do not create more vibration, more turbulence. The moment you judge you create disturbance.

KARINA» If there is a critical mass of people who are positive, can we as humanity make the quantum leap?

DONA» Well, that is the million-dollar question nowadays. I think humanity has made enormous leaps since the beginning. If you look at pre-history then we have made enormous progress. But we are still in the beginning of being human beings; there is still a long way to go. So by denying this world we are not being helpful. Wanting to escape to Nirvana or Shambhala is not helpful.

DIANA» You are saying we probably had to wait many lifetimes to be human this lifetime.

DONA» That I do not know. Then we get into all these belief systems of reincarnation and karma. That is not the way to go. Once you get into belief systems there is no end to it. You drown.

DIANA» But do you believe we are lucky to be here?

DONA» I think we are lucky to be here because the world is beautiful. It is, of course, a beautiful world because we are able to create and receive beauty. I think that our nervous system is constructed for specific reasons. The way we call the world beautiful is very different from what an insect would call beautiful or what a snake would call beautiful; we have different eyes, different ears. Each species has a different sense of beauty, a different sense of his world; each species lives in his own world, in his own fata morgana. A beetle has his own little fata morgana, an ant has his own little fata morgana... the plants have their own fata morgana. We have ours, which is in-built in the human DNA. The way we perceive the world is in-built in the human DNA. So I do not think that we can get out of it, but we can soften the edges by being aware that it is programmed in us.

J O S H » I was wondering what some of your earliest memories are? After the tales the other day of the tumultuous early years of your life I was wondering at what point you came into consciousness and started being aware of your surroundings. Do you have memories of the concentration camp?

D O N A » I do not have memories of the concentration camp. I used to have dreams of guns shooting and airplanes falling out of the sky, which were probably kind of replays from what I saw in the camp. The earliest memory I have is of the castle; me in my little bear suit going in the woods, then coming home with creepy little beetles and little slimy things to show to my mother, just roaming the woods all by myself. Getting lost in there, coming home hours later all dirty and full of slimy creatures. And my mother going: "Eeehh! What did you bring home this time?" The tiniest little insect, I would find it and bring home. The smaller the better. Vision, the pin pointed vision.

J O S H » How does sex fit into this whole equation as far as quantum moments is concerned. We spoke about how dancing can be something that people do, that they lose themselves in and achieve that one-to-one connection. What about sex?

D O N A » The quantum leap can be at any moment, anytime, anywhere. In the human world we live on a horizontal level: I do something for you, but you have to do something back for me. It is a give and take all the time; like a pirate situation we try to get more than we give out in general. So we are self generating. If you think of the universe as a giant electrical dynamo, then all we need is to plug in there, but we do not do that and so we try to get the electricity from somebody else. It can be by 'being in love', it can be in sex, it can be going to a concert, it can be whatever. This is always on the horizontal level. The vertical can happen any moment: either while having sex or while eating a hamburger or in the cinema. The moment you stop time, you have made that quantum leap. It has nothing to do with what you are doing. It is like the buildings: spirituality has nothing to do with a building or with a project; it has to do with that cutting out of time by being completely in total attention. Time is like a road with a car coming towards you in a straight line. As long as you see it coming towards you, that is the future. Then, for one instant, it is next to your shoulder and then it recedes behind your back: that is the past. The moment when the car is right next to your shoulder, so to speak, that is what we call the present. But the present, in reality, does not exist. It is the moment when the car, from coming towards you, recedes behind you. It comes towards you and then suddenly it recedes behind you. That is what we call the present. If there is no car coming and receding, you are in that moment, the eternal moment. To be in the eternal, you have to be in 'no-moment'.

Eyes of Innocence
Dona Holleman

10 Interview in Tepoztlan (Mexico), summer of 1999

DIANA » How important do you think the asanas are?

DONA » You mean the practice of the positions? I think that the body is the only real instrument we have for living in the universe. The brain is like a computer but the body is the one that touches everything else. If the body is not sensitive, if the body is a little dull, then you miss out on a lot of things because the body does not receive well. The body is like a radio receiver: it has eyes, ears, nose, tongue and skin. With this body, with these senses of knowledge, we receive the input from outside. Therefore, if the body is not clean and not clear, if the eyes and the ears are cloudy, we do not get a good view of what is happening outside. So the asanas serve to purify the body, to clean the body out, to make it a sensitive and intelligent organ of perception.

DIANA » I have heard you say that something happens to our brain with learning the asanas, or with yoga practice.

DONA » The brain is like a central computer and works by stimulation. If you do not stimulate the brain it atrophies, just like a muscle. If you do not use the muscle it weakens. By learning new postures all the time and going each time a little bit beyond what you know and what you can do the brain creates new connections. It creates new connections with the body and it creates new connections within the brain itself, so it keeps on exercising, it keeps on expanding, just like the body. The brain is just like the body, it needs exercise and that is what happens when you practice new positions. Not to stay with the same old positions, but to practice new positions all the time in order to stimulate the brain to create new connections.

DIANA » What is the state of attention?

DONA » In order to perceive the universe or reality you need to be completely attentive. The body needs to be a sensitive organ, because it is the only organ that we have. We are - in essence - perceivers. In order to perceive clearly there should not be any distraction.

DIANA » You were talking about that state of attention. You say it is important in the practice.

DONA » The state of attention is important not only in the practice, but it is important at all times because it is the only tool we have to understand ourselves in the world. When you practice the positions - the asanas - if you do not have the attention, then it is just going to be unorganized, the position it not going to be clear, it is not going to be cohesive. You need attention to bring out the perfection of the posture, which is not a futuristic thing, but something in the present, right in the moment itself. It is only by doing the posture with complete attention that you can bring the complete posture out of the body.

DIANA » How is that different from concentrating on doing something, wanting to achieve something by concentrating?

DONA » Wanting to achieve something by concentration involves the time aspect. You are not complete now but you want to have a good posture in the future, so you work towards it, which means that you will never get it. As long as you have to work towards something it is never going to happen. The difference between concentration and attention is that concentration is a pinpointing of the attention in one direction with the exclusion of everything else; therefore you only highlight a certain point. Attention is 360 degrees around, is everywhere at the same time, it does not include the future. When you talk about concentration, you are talking about the future. When you talk about attention you talk about no-future; you are completely in the moment itself.

DIANA » When you think about something you are not there?

DONA » When you think about something, you are not there because you are using words and images. Those words and images are things that you have learned in the past, they belong to the past. The present moment, on the other hand, is something that comes out of nowhere and disappears in a millionth of a second. The thinking process, the image process, the past can never catch up with it. As human beings our first - and maybe only - function is as perceivers. As perceivers we need to perceive this very moment, so if we allow the thinking process or the image process or memory or the past to come in between, then it is like putting a dirty glass in between you and what is happening now. You cannot see what is happening now, you only see the past.

KARINA » This has direct connection with the neo-cortex and the reptilian brain...

DONA » I am not sure what function of the brain... The new brain is mainly an electrical organ that has the function of coordinating all the data that we have. These data that we have are from the past. The onward process from childhood of the naming process, the labels that then acquire associations and experiences, these come between us as perceivers and the what-is-out-there.

DIANA » So language process is in the way?

DONA » On the one hand the language process is in the way; on the other hand it is necessary. At birth there are no names and no labels. As the labeling process starts it is like the computer Windows program: the first window the child sees when it is born is only pictures, colors, shapes. Then gradually another window is put in front of it, which is the same pictures, but with the names on them. Then the names get bigger and bigger and finally the names take on a life of their own and the first world is covered by the second one, the world of the names with the associations and memories. It is a necessary world because we need to communicate, we need to live. It is a man-made world that is made in order to be able to function and live in it. It is an agreement that everybody makes together to say: "OK, this is our world and we have to live together. I have to know what a car is." I simply have to know what a car is because I have to drive, I have to go to the office. If I do not know what a car is then I cannot go. It is an agreement that we make, that everybody makes together, in order to create this world where everybody knows what everybody else is talking about. In that way it is a necessary world. It is also a very monotonous and dull world because we always repeat the same old thing. As perceivers and as human beings we should remember that behind the man-made world there is still the 'wild world', where there are no words, no names, no time, no space, no future and no past. A world that is totally unknown, but covered over by this flimsy world of words.

DIANA » What we were talking about yesterday... about religions.

DONA » Religions and philosophies are based on words. These words create a whole fabrication of thoughts and feelings, which are completely man-made. Each religion, each philosophy has their ideas about what the universe is, has their ideas about what the present moment is. But they are only ideas; these ideas clash. That is why the history of human beings has been full of holy wars, of religious wars, because my God is better than your God, my God is the real God, your God is not the real God, and so my God has to destroy your God. It is a clash of words, of ideas, and will always divide people. While if you take the word away, the idea away, and you only have the world of sounds, like the bird sounds, and the trees, then there is no clash.

KARINA» Maybe all the mysticisms speak of the same thing, but the esoteric religions clash. Maybe the words divide reality into duality, but behind the words there is unity.

DONA» Exactly, there is only one thing: the world of bird sounds; but if I say: "There is the bird sound," I have already moved to the man-made world, because I recognize it as a sound, I recognize it as a bird sound; so already I have labeled it. The moment I label it, I have put something in between me and the sound.

DIANA» It stands in the way.

DONA» It stands in the way, because already I know what I am talking about: I am talking about bird song.

KARINA» So in essence we are all one, and whatever you do without words affects the whole.

DONA» I do not know if that person would affect the whole of the world. Probably it will, because everything is one thing. When you look at the world, you see empty space, and then you see a tree, and then another empty space and another tree. We think of the space in between as empty but in reality it is not empty at all. It is full of air and oxygen and particles. Personally I see the whole universe as a kind of jelly with objects like denser parts in the jelly, so if there is a shaking of one object in the jelly, then everything else will shake.

KARINA» I asked, because this is a principle of traditions like shamanism.

DONA» It is also modern physics. The famous phrase that if a butterfly flaps its wings in Tokyo there is a hurricane in Texas. The scientists themselves acknowledge that everything affects everything else. If you can toggle back and forth between the world of words, use the world of words - the man-made world - to live and then, when you need to get out, go in the other one. I think that if you really understand that the man-made world is a false world or a phony world, then I think there will not be any division because you know that division is only based on words; it is not based on the real thing. The real thing is one only.

DIANA » This 'not-doing' will connect us to that space?

DONA » Exactly. The world of words - the man-made world in which we live - is the world of 'doing'. We 'do' this: we make words, we make concepts: that is the 'doing' part. 'Not-doing' is a tricky word because if you say: 'not doing' it is still 'doing'. 'Not-doing' is not the opposite of 'doing'. 'Not-doing' is the absence of 'doing' which is not the same thing as the opposite.

DIANA » How would this work?

DONA » It works when you deeply understand that the world you live in, the world where you recognize things, where you work with things, know people, recognize people, that that world is the world that you are 'doing'. The understanding of that, the realization of that, the insight that it is a flimsy world put together by words, that realization is the 'not-doing', because that realization means that you can look behind that world. But you must have the realization; the realization is the 'not-doing'.

DIANA » In yoga and meditation... is the 'not-doing' important?

DONA » The word meditation in Latin actually means 'to think about'. It is often equated with the word 'contemplation'. The word contemplate comes from Latin and means 'to be in the temple', 'con templare'. You sit in a temple and you think about life. This is what most people understand as meditation. That is still a process in time at the end of which you hopefully reach enlightenment, freedom. It is a process; therefore it is still 'doing' and what you find at the end is of your own making. It is not the real thing. Mediation, as a time process, is still in the man-made world. The only thing which snaps you out of the time process and the man-made world is realization, to have the realization that whatever you do - even meditation, even yoga - is still within this one world. The moment you realize that it loses all its importance and then you are in the other world, automatically.

KARINA» That would be enlightenment?

DONA » The word enlightenment is such a dull word. These words like meditation and enlightenment are so loaded with meaning, with man-made meaning. Instead of meditation in which there is a time process, I say: "If you want to really stop all that, you also have to stop meditation." If you want to have a word which is close to meditation, you can say: 'meeting': you 'meet' life, you 'meet' the present moment. We never do that, because we always look at the label, we never look at the present moment. To 'meet' life, is that you say to the label: "OK, you just sit to the side and wait for a moment while I am going to have a meeting with this moment; you can come back afterwards."

KARINA» It means that you can be sitting meditating and be more in the world of the words than if you are washing the dishes.

DONA » Exactly.

KARINA» It is what the mystics call the 'witness'.

DONA » Exactly. The witness or the perceiver. Human beings are primarily perceivers, we perceive the universe.

KARINA» Would animals be more in the world of the moment than humans?

DONA » Maybe. I think that human beings, originally, were also more in the moment. I have heard about tribal people living in - quote/unquote - 'primitive conditions' that are extremely aware of everything that happens around them, a quality that so-called 'civilized people' have lost. Meditation has nothing to do with sitting and closing your eyes. It has to do with being totally aware of everything.

To be totally aware of everything, you cannot allow the world of the words to interfere. That means that you come to stillness. Total awareness, total attention is only possible in a state of total stillness, which is not quietness. Quietness - the borderline between quietness and dullness - is very thin, you never know where the borderline is, while stillness has a very sharp borderline. Stillness will never merge away into dullness, but quietness can easily merge into dullness.

DIANA » That is the still mind: the state of attention.

DONA » Yeah. Only a still mind can have full attention and vice versa. A mind, which is totally attentive to everything around, is a still mind. That is the real meditation, which I do not like as a word, so let us call it the real 'meeting'. At that moment you are a complete perceiver in the complete moment without past and without future.

KARINA» You always mention the natural world as an inspiration to your practice. Can you elaborate on that?

DONA » I look around and then I see what I can use at that moment in my practice. It can be a movement of an animal or anything. We come back to 'meeting' the moment: it is the same with the yoga posture. Most people do a yoga posture with a goal in mind: to reach a perfect posture, to reach the rule. Somebody makes a rule: you have to do the posture this way, and then you think you have to reach that posture. So again you allow time, a time lapse. In the time lapse you never see what goes really on. So attention and time are exclusive of each other. People do not understand that. When I practice yoga, I am fully attentive, I am not going anywhere, I am only doing that thing. There is no end goal.

DIANA » So it would be, in a sense, an excuse to be there? The whole practice would be a good way of just being there? That you can do it any other way but with the poses it is very clear?

DONA » The body needs to be finely tuned, so you need to eat good food - lots of fruit, salads - to have the body really clean and pure and the senses also clean and pure. The asanas help to do that and so does the breathing. They help to prepare the body. It is like having binoculars: if the binoculars are dirty you do not see much so you have to wipe the screen of the binoculars with a soft cloth. The asanas, the diet, and pranayama all serve as a soft cloth to make the perceiver sharp, clear.

DIANA » What would be the first thing you would require of your students, of a new student?

DONA » I do not require anything at all. Most students are not interested; they just want to have a workout. So you give them a workout. If you can go further it is good and then you can work on attention, to pay attention in the postures, in the class to what I am saying or showing. It is only through attention that you can distinguish the two worlds, the world of words, goals, future and time and the other world in which you only have full attention.

DIANA » What are the things that you hate about this yoga world?

DONA » Hate is a strong word. Almost everybody functions within this man-made world and so they are out for their own goals. There is a lot of phoniness going on in the sense of making promises within the man-made world. People say: "Oh, if you do my meditation you are going to get enlightened." That is a promise made by one man to another man, or one woman to another woman, but it is within the man-made world: it involves time, effort, the 'you-have-to-do-this, you-have-to-do-that' business. It is like saying: "If you take my train you are going to go to the top of the mountain." Selling, selling train tickets, marketing. That is what I do not like. They make the whole spiel, grow their hair, grow their beard, put on certain clothes, wear beads, Aum medals, all to advertise the fact that they are selling something. And it is easy to find buyers, because everybody is insecure. People are insecure, because they are navigating in a man-made world where everything is insecure, and so when they meet somebody who wants to sell them something, they are easily fooled.

KARINA » So it would all be to change your viewpoint instead of what you do.

DIANA » Exactly. It has nothing to do with what you do. It is something in the brain. To say it in a banal way, it is almost like you have a light switch in your brain. Usually you are on the man-made world switch and so all you have to do is to turn the switch to the other world, the not-man-made world. That switch is in the brain; it is again a question of being attentive. Full attention is the switch that switches you. What you are doing in the moment has nothing to do with it. You can be running a bath or washing dishes or can sit on your buttocks, close your eyes and grow your beard. It does not matter, everything depends on the switch.

KARINA» Going to the other world would be like reaching something divine?

DONA » No, then again you reach something. The divine is also a word; it is also loaded with man-made meaning. For instance, I always say that I am not a yogi. If you say you do yoga, 'yoga' means 'to unify', 'to unite', so this is why you are already out, because if you say you have to unify, it means you are acknowledging that there are two things, otherwise you would not have to unify. What I am saying, is that by turning the switch and being in a world where there is no label, no name and no time, there is no duality. You cannot combine it, you cannot unite. It is one thing. It is not reaching something, the divine. Everything is one; that is the simplest way you can say it.

DIANA » To go in a different direction... why is it important for you to teach yoga?

DONA » Why am I a yoga teacher?

DIANA » What made you?

DONA » I started with this thing before I did yoga, this idea of the 'not-doing'. I like working with the body, and I think it is important, a vital ingredient to be able to switch. Somebody who is not well, who is overweight, sick, tired, is preoccupied with the problem, so that it is difficult to switch the viewpoint, the vision. I teach, because when you do something and do it well, it is logical to teach it. It is the human heritage to see the beauty of the universe. You go in a place like this or you go out at night and look at the stars, you take it for granted because you know the words. But if you take the words away and you look at it as if it is the first time you see it then it is absolutely incredible. So you look at things around you like these trees, the mountains, as if you have never seen them before. Then it becomes something really incredible, very sharp, your attention is everywhere.

DIANA » You want to help people?

DONA » You cannot help another person. People have to help themselves. You can say that it is nice to do yoga, to do the postures and the breathing exercises. That is as far as you can go.

KARINA» But you can inspire people, like in my case, when I hear you talking about this you inspire me.

DONA » Sure, but that is as far as you can go. The person has to be open and has to do the work. I can only put the cookie on the table but you have to eat it.

DIANA » Do you find people are often lazy to go that step further?

DONA » Lazy and also afraid. It is much easier to stay within the words and to talk about Brahma and Vishnu, talk about reaching Nirvana. That is very easy, very pleasant. But to actually take everything out of your brain and disappear in a thin cloud, that is very scary.

DIANA » You say old people die of boredom...

DONA » Sure, they die of boredom because they think they know the world. They think they know everything. They have seen everything millions of times, they never see the thing for the first time and so they are never excited unless something really exciting happens, like a big earthquake. But if nothing dramatic happens, people lose the excitement of seeing something for the first time, for the one and only time. A leaf, when it moves, it will never, ever in eternity move in the same way again. If you think about it in that way, then you have to catch it as it moves, because it is never going to happen again that way. But if you think: "Oh, it will happen again billions of times," then you are bored.

KARINA» People also think that fate is not in their hands. That is a lack of responsibility, would you think?

DONA» It is a lack of responsibility. People do not want to be responsible for themselves and that is why they go in search for religions, philosophies, gurus, sects. It is a tango of insecurity, of uncertainty. The religions look for devotees, the gurus look for disciples, disciples look for a guru: it is a tango of insecurity.

DIANA» Why do you like tango and flamenco?

DONA» Because they are beautiful, exciting. They do something to your eyes and your brain when you look at them. Also because tango and flamenco, but also any other type of dance or music, can be an expression of this moment of total attention. Sometimes a dancer has a moment that you think: "Wow, that is different. That is the genuine thing."

KARINA» You do yoga from the energy body first.

DONA» To do a pose perfectly and also fast and without effort means you have to move your energy body a fraction faster than your physical body. That is what I do when I do a pose: I move my energy body first and then the energy body pulls the physical body.

KARINA» How did you learn this?

DONA» Partly by watching Douglas Fairbanks' movies, partly I had it in myself too. When I saw him move, I had never seen it in anybody. Maybe that was the thing that triggered me off: I never saw this kind of moving in anybody. When I saw his movies I recognized it.

DIANA» When did you see his movies?

DONA» About five years ago I started seeing them.

KARINA» So the attention calls the energy body.

DONA» Intent is the carrot you dangle in front of the energy body, and the energy body goes 'snap', and as it goes 'snap', it pulls the physical body.

KARINA» For that you have to have total stillness?

DONA» Without total stillness, without total attention, you cannot do that. Total stillness breeds total attention.

KARINA» And the breath would be the energy.

DONA» The breath is the fuel that pulls the energy body through the physical body.

DIANA» You mentioned that you do not like to say something and then be stuck with it.

DONA» Exactly, because life moves on. If you say something and for the rest of your life it has to be that way it is not possible, because everything is panta rei, like the Greeks used to say, the river is flowing. It is like putting a stick in the river and saying: "The stick is going to be there forever." It is not true, because the river will take the stick and move it away. Nothing, nothing stays.

DIANA» So you get inspiration all the time from different...

DONA» Sure, the process is ongoing, it never stops, never.

DIANA» That is the creative aspect of teaching?

DONA» That is the creative art. 'Creative' means you create something. You perceive all the time new things and then integrate them in your life and your practice.

KARINA» Do you think, like you said...

DONA» Exactly. The line of time is a linear line. There are six billion lines in this world, there are six billion people and each person has his own line. Each of these six billion people walks on his line: I walk on my line, you on your line. In my life I have done many things and all that put together is the point on my line where I am now. Everything that I did in my life I have in that point here. Then, maybe on the right side, I see somebody like Douglas Fairbanks, or a bird, or an animal, and I say: "OK, at this point in my line I can use that; I take it and I can use it, integrate it." Then that becomes part of the parcel and then I move on. Everybody is different, because everybody has a different history and is at a different pint on his particular line. That is why you cannot say: "Everybody should do yoga." I know some people who say: "Everybody in the world should do yoga." That is nonsense.

KARINA» Do you feel that some people want to hold on to Dona Holleman yoga?

DONA » Yeah, but it cannot be done.

DIANA » Yesterday you were talking about the production of knowledge...

DONA » Reproduce brain knowledge. In the yoga world knowledge has become very verbal. Verbal knowledge goes through the ear into the brain and that is where it stays. It is never translated into the body. The body gets knowledge by watching through the eyes; the knowledge of the body goes through the eyes, the knowledge of the brain goes through the ears. This is why, as a teacher, you have show the postures, because then the other person, his body, sees that. If you go to classes or you read a book, study from a book and you only have the words, they just congest the brain, but the body cannot produce it. The brain is very insecure, so if it has a lot of brain knowledge, a lot of words, it boosts itself and says: "Oh, I know everything. I know a lot." It goes completely out of balance. You become top heavy, your head is so heavy with all this stuff. But the body cannot produce it. So real knowledge is when the body can show it, not when the mouth can talk about it.

DIANA » Then we are doing something wrong here...

DONA » Of course these are all words but sometimes somebody may have that already in them and recognize the words. You can recognize the words but unless the body has the knowledge it cannot put it together from the brain knowledge.

DIANA » It would be like a false repeating...

KARINA» ...parrot.

DONA » Yeah, a parrot. For example, how many times I say: "Move your arm this way," and for ten years nothing happens. Then one day the student comes to me and says: "Oh, you know, this morning in my practice I discovered something really interesting: if I move my arm this way I have a different movement. Why did you never tell me?" and I say: "Listen, I have been telling you this for ten years but unless your body understands it it just goes in one ear and through the brain and out through the other ear."

KARINA» What is the role of having fun and humor?

DONA» I think that humor is the only real expression of being totally attentive. If you look at a bird and you 'know' it is a bird, then you can get bored; but if you do not 'know' that it is a bird and just look at it then it is something amazing and can be very funny, sweet, making you laugh. I think humor is one of the closest expressions of total attention.

KARINA» And being serious would be the contrary.

DONA» It is the opposite, it means you are closed, completely inside your brain; you do not see.

DIANA» Do you think yoga can make you this closed, serious...?

DONA» That happens often. It often has the opposite effect of what it should do.

DIANA» Why?

DONA» Because people are greedy. They are insecure and greedy and want to 'have' something. The greediness and the insecurity make that you want to 'do' something to the universe. You want to get enlightened, you as an entity want to be there and enjoy the fruit of your labor. You want to enjoy being enlightened. Instead, if you turn it the other way around and say: "OK, what can the universe do to me?" then it is a very different story. That is what I call total attention. Being totally attentive: "What does it do to me?" Not: "What do I do to it?" People are greedy, they want to enjoy the fruit of their labor, they want to get enlightened, reach nirvana.

KARINA» It is still based on aversion and attraction...

DONA» It is still based on the 'doing'.

DIANA» How would this attitude relate to the humbleness that it is been preached...?

DONA» The humbleness that is being preached is the most gruesome thing of all. It is absolutely appalling. If you practice humility or you tell a student to be humble, that is the grossest form of arrogance;

it is the gross side of arrogance.

KARINA» It is like a defense mechanism from arrogance, you would say...

DONA» No. It is arrogance. To 'be' humble is the final stage of arrogance, the last stage. In real humility you do not know that you are humble, you do not practice it. Real humility is when you are totally attentive and therefore you, as the perceiver, are not there. There is only the thing that you perceive. But then you cannot call it humility anymore, and you certainly are not 'being' humble.

KARINA» It is something that people want to show to the world.

DONA» Exactly, it is a show.

DIANA» Maybe you can finish what you were saying about humility being the grossest form of arrogance...

DONA» If you look at nature, plants and animals you see that nothing is humble. Everything has its place and everything is happy to have its place. There is not this false humility. Even the smallest animals or the smallest flowers will be all out there, saying: "Look, I am here." Humility is a human invention in order to keep people under, to keep people small, to control them. It is a control issue. The person who wants you to be humble wants to control you.

DIANA» That is probably why religions...

DONA» Of course, religions have always have kept the masses in a low status because then they can control them. If somebody is intelligent and independent you cannot control that person and then you have a problem.

DIANA» Let us talk about the seven vital principles.

DONA» When you see people practicing the positions, the asanas, the first thing you see, if you really observe them, is that they have no idea about their bodies, about the structure of the body, about the cohesion of the body. Everything is fragmented: "Do this here, do this there, move your foot, move your hand," everything is local and fragmented; there is no overall picture. So the first thing is to get the body together, to learn about the body; not about the asanas, but to learn about the body. If you want to practice an asana you are dealing with a body that is already full of tensions, full of the past. This body is not ready to receive a new thing. It is like having a desk full of papers and you want to put one more paper on it. It is a mess. In that case, the best thing to do is to get all the papers out of the way and put only one paper on the desk. This is exactly the first idea of the practice, that you have to learn, first of all, to relax the body. This does not mean Savasana; it does not mean going limp or go to sleep. It means that you get all the tensions of the body out of the way. You relax the parts that are stiff from inside. The same goes for the brain; you relax the brain too, get all the stuff out of the brain: empty out the body and empty out the brain. Then you say: "OK, now we are going to do a posture." Which can be any posture, it does not matter which one. Because there are no other thoughts to compete with it is very strong. If you are busy and then say: "Oh, by the way, I also want to do Paschimottanasana," then that thought is very weak, because it is drowning in a lot of other things. But if you get everything out of the way and then you say: "I want to do Paschimottanasana," then it is very powerful. That is what I have called 'intent'. So after the relaxation of the body and the relaxation of the mind you have intent, which is the picture you give to the energy body, or the carrot you give to the energy body in order to get the energy body's appetite up. The energy body likes to move; this you can see very easily if you put music - dance music on - nobody can sit still. You try to have a room with a hundred people and put dance music on and see if somebody is sitting still; nobody will be sitting still. Because the dance music invites the body to make movements. So the picture is the invitation for the energy body to make a movement, to make a posture. And then the energy body moves and pulls the physical body with its enthusiasm, with its energy. That is intent. Then, once you get to the physical body and the actual position you have to see where the body is in relation to the gravitational line. Gravity is at its strongest at the level where it collides with the earth, so where the body collides with the earth that is where gravity is most usable. You have to let that part which is colliding with the ground, with the earth, ride downwards with gravity, on the gravity force; that then will generate the opposite force which is called the rebounding force, which is the same force as the gravitational force but it goes in the opposite direction. In a way, the more you go down with the part which collides with the ground the more the rest of the body goes upwards because it is propelled upwards by the rebounding, anti-gravitational force. That is called 'rooting'. Then, in order to make the movement smooth and fluid, you have to align the joints in such a way, that the rebounding force can go through them without getting stuck in angles, so it is round lines in the joints, so that the anti-gravitational rebounding force can shoot easily through the body. That is called 'connecting'. Then you add the breathing, in order to pull this rebounding force even stronger through those connecting lines. That turns the whole movement into an elongating movement. The body elongates.

DIANA » Those are the seven principles?

DONA » Those are the seven principles of practice. This is the way I practice.

DIANA » The same when you teach.

DONA » That is the way that I teach. Therefore there is no effort involved because you do not use force, you do not use only your muscle power. You use all the forces available: the gravitational force, the anti-gravitational rebounding force, the breathing, making the alignment in such a way that there is no obstruction for the energy to flow. So you use a very small amount of the effort you otherwise would employ by doing the position.

DIANA » That is how the asana becomes alive.

DONA » And easy and smooth and fast.

KARINA » The energy body always precedes the movement?

DONA » Yes..

KARINA » Even if you are not conscious of it?

D O N A » No. Normally the energy body is synchronized with the physical body and has a minor role in the sense that people put the entire accent, all the emphasis, on the physical body. The thing to do is to kind of separate the two and then move the energy just a little faster than the physical body; then the energy body will pull the physical body through very fast.

D I A N A » What if somebody has a physical problem and cannot do one asana or any asana. What happens with the physical limitations of the body?

D O N A » Everybody has physical limitations. There is not one person who has not. The idea is to look at those limitations, to see how much you can do without forcing through them. Find a way around them or find a way to dissolve them from the inside.

K A R I N A » To work around them could you insert those concepts of the mind being carnivore and the body being vegetarian?

D O N A » Predator... There are two things involved in the human being; one is the body and the other one is the energy person inside the body. The body comes originally from the ape family, from the great apes: chimpanzees, gorillas. These belong in the realm of vegetarian animals. They may eat insects on occasion but mainly they eat leaves, flowers, fruits and nuts. The body has the fear of a vegetarian animal that is being eaten by a predator. The mind, on the other hand, is aggressive - the new brain. The mind is always trying to steal things, to get things, to eat them. The mind is a predator, so when we approach the body with the predator mentality of "you have to do this, and you have to do that posture," the body will be afraid and will react. Therefore the mind has to step back and allow the body to do the posture, not say: "you have to do this, you have to do that."

D I A N A » Has yoga's essence been lost with it being so popular in the West?

D O N A » I think so. In the first place, when you bring a culture over into another one - like an Indian culture into Western culture - a lot gets lost anyway and confused. In the second place, if then you introduce it to the masses it gets more lost. I think the same thing has happened to Karate and Judo. All these things were originally disciplines in order to make the body a real good instrument. But now it is just for the masses, everybody wants to do yoga, everybody wants to do Karate, and so it has become rather superficial. Which is OK, for a lot of people that is OK; but for some people is not enough.

DIANA » How to find its essence again?

DONA » Awareness is the key: the awareness of the postures, the awareness of yoga, the awareness of your body. For instance, what I see very often is that people are supple, young, strong - they do a nice posture, but when they come out of the posture they just slump, they walk in a tired way. This means that the awareness is very limited, only in a particular moment, in a particular posture, but for the rest it is gone. You have to cultivate a twenty-four hour awareness pattern in which part of you is aware of your body, is aware of what you do with it, is aware of everything else. That is the key.

DIANA » Why do you think the West is so hungry for all these Eastern philosophies?

DONA » I think that the West is ahead of the East. The East is roller coasting on past glory. The philosophy in India, I do not think it exists now. It is past glory. Everybody in India talks about the Bhagavad Gita as if they themselves wrote it. I do not think they know what it is all about. They have to go through the material way of thinking and then find something real, something new. We in the West are coming out of the material thing. We have a complete philosophy background: the Greeks, the Romans, we have a lot of philosophy, plenty, more than enough. Then we wandered into the material, but now we are coming out of it and have to find something real, something new, not just a word 'philosophy', and certainly not a philosophy that belongs to another culture, another time. But a lot of people - either because they are snobbish, or because they do not know - turn to the East as if the East has the answer. It is always: "The grass is greener over the hill."

KARINA» How do you explain that some people are born surrounded by philosophy and some people are born somewhere where they do not have anything?

DONA » I do not think that is a valid question. Some of the American presidents were born in families where they had to bring newspapers around for many years before they could climb their way up into the presidential palace. It is not a question of where you were born. It is a question of how much energy you have inside to go out and do something new.

DIANA » We were talking about people who want to be saints and get away from all the mundane things... why do you think that happens?

DONA » Because people do not understand. What is sacred and what is mundane? Who decides what is what? You have to understand that it is human beings who decide everything. Is there a label on your forehead that says: "I am a Mexican Jew?" No, it is not there. So if you think that you are a Mexican Jew it means that somewhere that label is inside your head. It is certainly not on your forehead.

DIANA » Do you think we should get rid of all those stamps?

DONA » We have to get rid of them, because as long as we have those stamps, as long as we have all those ideas, we are going to have problems. Look at Yugoslavia, the Albanians and the Serbs. I cannot tell the difference between them and yet they kill each other because one is an Albanian and the other one is a Serb. It is the same thing with the mundane. People say: "Oh, going to the movies is mundane, and going to church is sacred." Who decides? Who decides whether one building with a cross on it a sacred building and another building is not? Who decides that? We do. And our decision is totally arbitrary. You may take a Bushman who has never seen a church or a cinema: he would not be able to tell the difference. It is only what you have learnt to say and do and that is totally arbitrary. It is like saying: "Killing people is bad." That is an arbitrary law, which sounds wonderful in peace times, but in war everybody is sent out to kill the 'enemy' and that is OK, as long as it for the Patria. Dying for the Patria is the highest moral thing you can do. Who decides that? Who is right? If you have a bird that lives in Scandinavia, when it gets cold, it wants to go to Africa. It flies over Denmark, over Germany, over Austria, over Italy, over the Mediterranean and it ends up in Africa. Does he have to stamp his passport to go over? He doesn't even know that there is a frontier. He just flies, so the frontier is man-made.

DIANA » So the solution is to not have language, these stamps?

DONA » No, that is not the solution. The solution is to have the man-made world but to take it with an enormous amount of salt, to know it is arbitrary. To know that you have to live in it, but never take it too seriously. Never take yourself seriously as an Italian or a Mexican and never take yourself serious as a Catholic or whatever. It is only man-made. When you die, you die, and you are nothing.

DIANA » Do you think the emotional body clashes with the energy body?

DONA » Yes, sure. But the emotional body is built and fed by the mental body, by thought, by ideas. If you do not have ideas about something you cannot have an emotional reaction. Emotion is never an action, it is always a reaction, and the reaction is always against something that has a word for it.

DIANA » So we go back to language...

DONA » You go back to language. If you get out of the world of words and ideas, then there is no emotional reaction, because emotion belongs to the world of language, not to the world of real things.

DIANA » You talked about the front and the back part of the body...

DONA » The front part of the body is the part that you can see. Usually everything is done on the front. All your gestures are on the front. The back part has more to do with the Medulla oblongata, with the back brain, with the spine. It does not have all that emotional content that the front has.

DIANA » So when we are aware of the back part we...

DONA » Yeah, you are in a more silent part of the body.

KARINA» You talk about an insight...

DONA » Yeah, not to get away from it.

KARINA» That can be misunderstood.

DONA » Not to get away from it, you just have to see that they have their place. It is like a child. The child has its place in the larger family, but if suddenly this child gets up and takes over the whole household it is out of hand. Everything has its place: the man-made world has its place, thought has its place, but - like the child - it should stay in its own room and not take over the whole house. The brain is only a very small part of us. The body as an organ of perception is the biggest part of us.

DIANA » Indians put down the body...

DONA » Well, look what happened in Indian society. Indian society is an outcome of that way of thinking, the caste system. Baby girls get thrown away on the garbage heap when they are born; poverty, misery. That way of thinking breeds problems.

KARINA» Do you think that the cells of the body have intelligence...?

DONA » Definitely. The physicists also say that every particle has intelligence. What Einstein said and which he himself did not like was that when two particles in the universe collide the knowledge that they have, the information that they have is shared by them. So to say it really simply: if one particle has a headache and collides with the other one the other one has instantly also a headache. Of course, in the universe all the particles have collided since the Big Bang because they keep moving around. So in the universe everything has collided. The whole universe shares the same information including the body. Each cell of the body has all the information it needs. You do not need a guru, you do not need a book, you do not need anything, your body contains all the information that it needs. Your guru lives right inside the cells of your body.

DIANA » You have to let it come out.

DONA » You have to listen to it.

Behind the scenes

By *Toni Montez*
Friend and art director of the documentary film "Eyes of Innocence"

The cast of characters

The Crew

Diana Eichner	*director and perfectionist*
Daniel Frydman	*her husband, producer and master chef*
Josh Ferrazzano	*producer, cell-phoner and joker*
Anette Uziel	*photographer, creative jewelry designer*
Juan Pablo Capella	*assistant photographer, gentle man*
David Bower	*gaffer, mountain climber*
Chris O'Connell	*clapper, helper*
Karina Eichner	*replacement cook and clown*
Kate Rabinovich	*off location, executive producer, money raiser and organizer*

The Cast

Dona Holleman	*star and inspiration*
Toni Montez	*ancient hanger on*
The crew	
The juggler	

Others

Brandy	*make-up superb*
Dimitri	*her son*

Location

Grand Teton National Park, Teton Village, Jackson, Wyoming and environs.

DIANA is a thoughtful, quiet young woman recently married to Daniel. Diana and her sister Karina are from Mexico City, they graduated from Dona's second teacher training course last year 2000, held in Berkeley, CA and that is how we knew each other. Diana studied at NYU Film School. Later she returned to Mexico, graduated in communication studies and majored in film. She and Daniel are now students in Florida where Diana is studying Spanish literature. Diana had worked diligently to write up and plan the filming. She and Daniel had made an earlier trip to look for locations in the Teton area. It was clearly a large amount of work that she had done before we even landed in Jackson, WY. Diana is devoted, motivated, inquiring, creative and persistent. Necessary attributes for a filmmaker. Also she proved to be flexible as things did not always go according to her well-laid plans.

DANIEL, Diana's husband, is a charmer, a delightful, humorous, fun young man whom you could easily imagine bouncing off the walls. He seemed to be everywhere at once and was busy taking care of everyone. Daniel was trained as a chef in France and found it easy to cook elaborate four or five course meals, as well as to cater to each and every person's personal needs. With his red hair, bear hug qualities and high energy Daniel is difficult to miss or to overlook. Busily supporting and helping Diana with the unexpected, Daniel managed to take good care of all of us and seemed to enjoy the task. Daniel is studying hotel management.

JOSH, the producer, hails from New York City and with his cell phone, leather jacket and dark sunglasses seemed to be in the wrong environment. Be not fooled. Despite his constant long distance phone calls from the barren fields in the snow or where we happened to be, Josh really knew how to handle a canoe and was not at all unfamiliar with an uncivilized terrain. Josh is a filmmaker as well and has directed a feature with unusual images which plays in New York clubs. Josh enjoyed fooling around and joking, when he wasn't on the phone. Effective in his job, Josh located the necessary equipment, obtained the paperwork so that we were able to move here and there.

ANETTE, our photographer, is a friend of Diana's, also from Mexico City but working in Miami creating beautiful, expensive jewelry. She has had past experience as a film photographer and was pleased to take on this role for Diana. Annete is competent and quiet. For someone of her small stature she had little difficulty handling the large and awkward camera.

JUAN PABLO, who assisted Annete with the camera and was there to be of help each moment, came especially from Mexico City to take part in this venture. Juan Pablo is a gem, quiet, sweet and mild mannered. He was willing to be of assistance to anyone. This was true of all of the group, but his shyness seemed to emphasize his helpfulness. I couldn't imagine anyone not being charmed by him and I probably was further impressed because he is an animal lover.

DAVID is a young man of many talents and many jokes. Clearly someone to have with you when you are unaware of what might happen. David also comes from the NYC area where he shares an apartment with his girl fiend, who also shares his love of mountain climbing and hiking. As with the others, he had never been to the Tetons and he planned to return for some quick trips up and down the peaks. David is also an accomplished wood worker and furniture builder.

CHRIS is another interesting, talented person, who had lived in Japan and taught English there while learning some Japanese in the process. Chris is an avid reader of unusual, new literature. This encouraged me to investigate these authors. A person of varied interests who had much to contribute. He is quiet and thoughtful, enjoying himself in a more reflective, observant manner. Chris was planning to start graduate school at UC Berkeley this fall and has been accepted in their journalism program.

Last but not least, **KARINA**, Diana's sister. Karina joined us midway through the project, planning to take over for Daniel as he had to return to school before we were finished. Karina lives in Mexico City with her husband. She works there as a psychologist and teaches yoga as well. Karina is also attending school and writing her thesis. In contrast to Diana, Karina is loquacious. She enjoys talking, joking, playing, having a fun time. She is a delight, informed and an accomplished photographer.

Introduction

This was written as a personal journal to record my views on this new experience of being involved in the making of a film. The characters all exist but unfortunately the events have been modified or deleted to protect the innocent.

It all began when two of Dona's students proposed making a film about her. It would not be a yoga teaching film or a yoga demonstration film. It was to incorporate Dona's ideas, her metaphors, her philosophy as well as the yoga. This film was to extend and appeal to a greater audience than just the yoga community.

Kate began a money raising campaign while Diana commenced work on a script. Not too long after, Dona and I embarked on this new 'expotition', as Pooh bear would say.

The Yellow Brick Road

On a lovely, sunny day in October Dona and I arrived at the Jackson, Wyoming airport in a small plane, to be greeted on the tarmac by the camera crew. Being filmed and introduced we were then rudely pointed at, you and you, and told to move into the airport by the airport ground crew. The film crew, for mysterious reasons, was exempt. The airport at Jackson, Wyo. is the only airport in the US within a National Park, the Grand Teton National Park. Quite a spectacular landing field it is with the mountain range in the background.

We quickly learned about the young film crew members, none of whom knew all the others. Josh and Chris had driven a rented truck from Salt Lake City with most of the film equipment. Josh had met Diana in NYC six years ago when they were in film school together. He knew and recommended David as a gaffer who soon became the sound man. Chris came along for the ride and to help out in any way he could. Anette, came as the photographer, a role for which she has had quite a bit of experience. Juan Pablo came from Mexico City to assist Anette. Daniel, as well as taking care of everyone's food needs, was willing to be of assistance wherever he might be needed.

Diana knew everyone but David, Chris and Juan Pablo. Josh knew David, Chris, Diana, Daniel and Karina. David and Chris knew only Josh. Juan Pablo knew no one. Anette, Dona and myself knew Diana and Karina.

In a short period of time we were aware of how competent, intelligent, responsible and fun this group of twenty-year olds is. I was amazed at how well everyone got along, how cooperative they were with each other. I made a comment to Diana about my observation. She said that before we were finished there would probably be outbreaks and some exposed emotions. Film making has a reputation for the unexpected.

Initiation

Early our first morning Brandy came to apply make-up to both Dona and me… to make us filmable. For Dona that is relatively easy. Brandy had a great deal of experience with film and television make-up and watching her in action was riveting. We sensed that we were over made up, too much this or that, even though we had been told that it was necessary in order to look natural for the camera.

We joined everyone in the large house that had been rented to house the crew. A lovely, light filled house perfect for our needs and with ample space for housing everyone comfortably. The furniture had been moved to the side of the spacious living room making space for whatever was to transpire there.

Daniel was busy with the meal preparations and finishing up with breakfast. He was quickly recognized for his expertise in the culinary arts and generosity in his responses to the likes and dislikes of his charges. He was busily preparing a list of the provisions to be acquired and with Josh would buy supplies, run errands and fill the requests of all. No small tasks.

Dona was to be interviewed that morning inside the living room with the lights, sound equipment and the paraphernalia of filming. It was something we were being introduced to and with which to become familiar. Listening to Dona speak and watching how things were handled, as well as being able to see the screen which would indicate how the filming would look, was fascinating. While Dona was speaking at some length about her philosophical ideas, it was pleasing to me to see the crew become interested and somewhat mesmerized by her words and ideas.

That day I was also briefly filmed outside. Although for me it seemed like a long period of time. Admittedly being filmed did not feel comfortable or natural to me and I hoped that would not be too obvious. My impression of individuals interviewed in documentaries is that they often do seem at ease, natural and readily able to express themselves. How is that done? Is it the ability of the director, the photographer or the passion of the speaker? I was not anxious to see myself and was pleased when it was finished. Diana, at that time, seemed like a relentless questioner and I could see how perhaps someone would or could say things that they had no intention of saying just in hopes of bringing an end to the process. It was easy for me to defuse the ordeal by realizing that I was only an on-looker and not a significant player in this event.

This first day was beautiful and sunny in the Jackson Hole area and I had a feeling that it might have been somewhat misused as this lovely weather might not last.

The woods

Our first day in the great outdoors, we drove en masse with rental truck and cars to a lovely area where we were to hike, talk and film. This area was just outside the Teton National Park and a film crew with equipment was not a small expedition into the woods. Daniel had provided this caravan with munchies and liquids so that hunger in the forest would not be a complaint.

The area we were in is spectacular and the group paused to discuss and film while I could not resist moving quietly onward to explore. I was not to venture off as Daniel called to restrain me from going too far afield on my own. The two of us sat quietly by a creek enjoying the calm and the beauty of the place. I did manage later to see deer as I wandered ahead of the group. Later we reached a spectacular space which actually had been discovered by Diana and Daniel when they came early to check out locations. It was below the trail and provided handsome trees for handstands, beautiful backdrops, sunny skies and impressive rocks. Here more filming was accomplished.

At the top of this trail was an overlook, a large lake situated below, high mountain crags in the background. There was an impressive rock, a huge one that we could climb on and that the mountains framed in the background. Dona did some sitting poses on the rock looking as though she was elevated in the sky. Later, in a nearby spot, she did back bends, with the lake shimmering far below in the background. This also was an impressive location and the poses moved so freely as though part of the environs.

Suddenly Daniel and Josh had an emergency, remembering that they had to be at the Fed Ex office in Jackson before closing. So they had to run back to the van and to town. Then it started to rain a bit and we all rushed back, down the trail and eating our lunch as we did so. During this change of pace it was necessary to establish who was going to go where, when, in which car and with whom. Logistics are a major part of this movie making business and some of it is done on the spot and on the run.

Dona's day in the snow

Dona was to be filmed standing on her head outdoors. The chosen day was not sunny and inviting. In fact, we were all well bundled up with multiple layers of clothing, the heater in the van was put on high heat and velocity. As we searched the selected area for the best spot the weather became increasingly grey and damp. There was, by the time we selected an area, thick wet snow resting heavily on the grasses, weighing them down.

Places were arranged on the field, like markings on a stage floor for the placement of the actors. A temporary tent was erected for the camera and the crew. When they were prepared then a mat and blanket was quickly placed on the ground for Dona. She then doffed her heavy warm coat, extra sweaters and cap to invert herself in yoga clothing. Meanwhile the snows continued to thicken the grey air with wet clumps. Dona later reported that doing headstand was difficult with the snow falling into her eyes and blinding her, to say nothing of the cold temperature.

This scenario continued for quite some time with Dona, between takes, huddling in her coat in fetal position in an attempt to retain as much body heat as possible. It was necessary now and then to get a heat fix in the van where the dampness could be temporarily overcome. Then again back into the field and the thick, wet day. Dona was definitely a trooper, the show did go on, and Diana managed to get yet another shot.

Following this day of unmitigated wet and cold, Dona went home and straight into a hot tub to soak and then to bed. It was a wise move. I brought her some dinner from the house and then she quickly went to sleep. Usually Dona worked evenings planning what she would like to discuss and what she and Diana could incorporate the following day. Not on this particular evening.

Following this experience Dona took advantage of any opportunity to tease us and to assure us that any complaints we might have were naught in comparison to her ordeal of exposure to the elements, on her head, no less. None of us could compete with that, of course.

Juan Pablo, who was experiencing snow for the first time, joined the others in the creation of an imaginative and unique snowman which managed to retain its form and personality, decorating the back landing of the house for several days.

The juggler

This is the story, which Dona tells about the simple, uneducated young man who lives in a monastery and is ridiculed by the priests for his inability to read and write. Yet he was devout and sincere. He wanted to be able to present a gift to the Madonna but knew not what he could contribute. Then he knew what to do and in the dark of night he went to the Madonna. He stood before her and with tears in his eyes he offered his juggling performance, throwing flaming brands into the air to retrieve and throw again before her. The priests had followed him and as they watched were appalled by his performance. They were on the verge of interrupting him when the Madonna came from her perch in her niche, and used the blue mantle of her dress to wipe the tears from the juggler's face.

This simple story was to be filmed and Daniel had advertised in the Jackson, Wyoming newspaper for a juggler. Diana had e-mailed me with the concern that perhaps a juggler was not to be found in all of Jackson Hole. Consequently she was not prepared for the number of phone calls and e-mails which they received in their home in Florida. One message, left on their answering machine, baffled them. The person who had called, extolled his virtues as an individual trained in conflict resolution and familiar with escorting foreign dignitaries throughout the Jackson Hole area. Diana phoned him with great curiosity, to inquire more about his abilities and to let him know that what they really wanted was someone who could actually juggle.

Diana became overwhelmed with the response and finally pretended ignorance, allowing Daniel to handle the calls. In the end the choice was narrowed to two possibilities. When Diana and Daniel came to Jackson to interview the jugglers, they had pretty much decided on one, then they met Eric. Eric was working at a meat packing company where hunters brought their prey. In the summer he had worked for the Sierra Club in San Francisco and this curious juxtaposition of employment was to further his understanding and broaden his viewpoint. He was young, tall, dark, bearded and handsome, with a slight limp. Eric had been taught to juggle as a young boy by his mother to help him overcome his cerebral palsy. He was adept at multiple balls, juggling pins and much more juggling than was needed for the filming.

Outside in the dark of the crisp night with flaming brands the scene was filmed.

String Lake

Hoping for better weather we arose pre-dawn to take canoes and the rented raft to String Lake to film there. This was a day I had been looking forward to as I dearly love to canoe. It was becoming light when we put canoes and the raft into the water. The sky was not as clear as we had hoped and the mountains were veiled in mist and clouds. But the lake was still and the air crisp and pleasant.

The lake is shallow, waist deep at the most, not threatening or dangerous in any sense. We maneuvered the canoes and the raft through the narrow inlet to the second part of the lake where a sandbar was to be used for photographing asanas. Dona was not pleased with the sandbar as it was cold and damp.

We journeyed to the far shore to enjoy some breakfast and watch the mountains slowly break through the mist and present themselves in their elegant magnificence. It was here that the grey jays flitted through the trees and one was bold enough to eat out of my hand numerous times. It was here also, just off shore, that the act of creating and filming a vortex was in process. David, wearing fishing boots, stood in hip deep water and with a canoe paddle attempted to create a whirlpool. Chris was standing by to throw a leaf into the vortex to illustrate how individuals get trapped in the whirlpool of ideas from which they find it difficult to extricate themselves. With most of us standing on the bank and giving suggestions to Dave, he was inundated by conflicting commands. Do it fast, do it slow, do it ahead of the leaf, below the leaf, behind the leaf, until he stood helpless with the paddle out of the water unable to move. We all laughed with the absurdity of the situation. In the end, the vortex was never captured, elusive as it might very well have been.

Most of us had returned to our base of operations where we had originally launched our raft and canoes. Daniel was busily preparing a fire in order to create a warm lunch for us. The sun was bright now though the air still nippy. Karina had taken off alone in a canoe to test her new found paddling skills. She went to join the few who remained at the other end of the lake. Unbeknownst to anyone, the other canoe had gone tippee canoe into a few feet of water. Karina was the only witness to the stunned faces she found soon after the incident. So it was a quick return to the original shore and a search for a change of clothing.

The Million Dollar Cowboy Bar

On the town square in Jackson, Wyoming is the famous Million Dollar Cowboy Bar with its brilliant neon bucking bronco sign. A colorful, large establishment with gold and silver dollars embedded in the bar and saddles lined up to replace the usual bar stools. Evidently the Cowboy Bar had been filmed in many a flick and our presence fortunately did not create too much attention. As we were not readily recognizable that also helped.

Dona and I were filmed multiple times entering the drinking spa and finding our way to the unused bar on one side of the room where we settled into our saddles. We did our best to appear jaunty and comfortable in these unusual circumstances. After ordering some red wine from Josh, we proceeded to tell each other our memorable horseback riding experiences. Dona, as a child, riding freely through the tea plantations in Java. My memory involved a bruised bottom from a long day trail ride with my teen-age children in New Zealand. While it snowed outside we enjoyed the warmth and fun of this experience.

Dona had been philosophizing during the filming about reality tunnels. How we are all programmed from an early age by our parents, our environment, our language, our culture and with all we come into contact. What we think of as reality is biased, not real at all. As our conversation moved into our recent experiences of the aging process, I thought of the dichotomy of the outward persona and the inner being. Realizing that others perceive me as old, while inwardly I feel quite young, is a reality tunnel that I find myself living with each day. This presents me with an interesting dilemma.

Filming is a long, slow and not particularly stimulating process. I'm not certain if it was to our advantage to be as unsophisticated about it as we were but perhaps the newness and our lack of knowledge helped us to remain curiously interested. A great deal of patience is involved and much time is spent in preparation. Then, of course, the repetition, not necessarily of doing a shot over again and again, but also doing it from a different angle or from a new perspective involves time and more time. It was a different experience, not necessarily one I would choose to do often.

Raindrops keep falling on my head

Dona has a process of energy-walking. I suspect she developed this technique from her own observations, from the changes which occur when the center of gravity is consciously located in the pelvis, from the theories that she has developed in her practice of yoga and also from observing how Douglas Fairbanks, Sr. moved so lightly in his films.

If you sit at a sidewalk café in the States and just observe the passers-by, you will notice that many people lead with their heads as they walk. You won't see this if you are observing citizens in Indonesia. It seems that in the Western societies we tend to reside in our heads and move forward with our noses. Not everyone does this. Our center of gravity is located in the pelvis, known as the hara in Japanese martial arts. If we are centered in our hara, the upper body is light and lifted and the head is moving upward rather than forward. This creates a much different stance and a more erect posture. It allows a greater freedom throughout the entire body.

In yoga poses the pelvic area is firm, the spinal column elongated so that the body can twist and/or bend in relation to the stability in the hara. The movement should be an upward one accomplished with ease and lightness. The energy then can flow and move rather than sink. Watching Douglas Fairbanks in action, it seems almost as though he defies gravity. His ability to leap, to leave the earth seems more akin to Peter Pan than to a real individual. Most of us are heavy and we succumb to the pull of gravity, we are devoid of the lightness which perhaps we never realized we have.

Diana had planned to have all of us learn and illustrate Dona's process. She had located a lovely area where the mountains would present an impressive backdrop. It happened to be a wet, grey, dense day with zero visibility. No sparkling mountain peaks to highlight and to magnify our uplifted steps. Nonetheless, all of us joking and jostling in the cold and wet to keep warm, Dona gave us instructions. First just to walk in our normal manner. Then to allow ourselves to be pulled from the center of the pelvis as though by an invisible line. Walking became so much easier that we found ourselves almost running. Little effort was involved. Watching and comparing ourselves on film would be revealing.

Then we went in search of a road moving far into space, fading into the horizon or more likely on this moist day, into the mist. "...because I'm free, nothing's worrying me..."

At the river

We had stopped singing "Raindrops Keep Falling on My Head" in an effort to bring about warmer, sunnier weather. Hey, it worked, the rain stopped until after the filming was completed.

On a sunny day we headed for the Snake River. Diana and Daniel had found a spot on the river and not too far from the parking area. That was recommended, as the terrain was rocky, full of colorful, difficult-to-walk-upon stones. Dona was perched on a large, smooth boulder at the edge of the water, the river moving along behind her, a pool with tiny frogs alongside the boulder, while the director and crew did their thing. Discussing and determining how to do whatever it was that they wanted to do. Meanwhile several fishing rafts headed downstream, a pair of eagles circled nearby and a coyote jumped in the grassy area across the water.

The scene was idyllic. The water sparkled and glistened and made a great deal more noise than was expected in such peaceful, isolated surroundings. It looked quite benign although the signs warned not to go afloat without an experienced rafter to lead you. One could only wonder what rapids or dangers lay unseen downstream.

While Dona was interviewed sitting like a warmly clad water nymph on her rock, I ventured up and down the river. Wary of bears, which we never saw, I enjoyed the sun, the river and the multicolored rocks. During a 'between takes' period Karina, Josh and I hopped across the rocks, attempting to keep our feet dry, or at least I did; I was not as adventuresome as they were. Explorations were limited by the river itself, and its banks were not always passable.

On one of our final days we returned to film high above the river where Dona walked her edge between two extremes. The river being true to its name, snaked slowly in a curvaceous meander far below us in the distance. The Teton National Park is full of these exceptional vistas back-dropped by the longest, incredibly beautiful range of peaks. The park is part of the largest wilderness area in the United States which includes Yellowstone Park and adjacent national forest areas.

Nearby was an old weathered tree, stark and bleached grey, perched at the edge of the cliff side. Josh insisted on climbing up the limbs, a precarious act because the tree looked dry, brittle and primed for breakage. A double trunk at the base of the tree provided a comfortable seat for Dona while she was interviewed further.

Things had gone well and we were drawing to a close.

Muted and bold

On one of our last days of shooting we headed back to the woods. A handsome, huge boulder had been noticed not far from the road. It was on this rock that Dona was to stand in her muted Robin Hood-colored outfit to blend into the environs. Dona stood in tree pose, her arms extended overhead to reflect the growing, rooted trees which surrounded her. The calmness of the pose with the stillness of the forest merged together into a natural composition free of dissonance. There were five people on this rock, assisting, angling light on Dona's face, adjusting, commenting and also at times filming.

A truck and a van stopped to gawk and question. Other people, probably locals, drove by as though irritated with another film crew trespassing on their road. The area was beautiful with the fall foliage already blanketing the earth; mosses and lichen decorating the rocks, a harmonious peace found only in such a natural habitat.

Later we moved from the darkness of the forest to a more open, expansive vista. Dona was to drop back from a standing position onto the ground and into a back arch. The brilliance of the mountains in the background was to be framed by her rounded, arching body. The spectacular mountain peaks were also to contrast with her arching body. In contrast to the morning's shoot, which emphasized the harmony of self and nature, this filming was to display the beauty of the pose, highlighted with the magnificence of the mountains. Here Dona wore a wine-colored leotard to contrast with the blue of the sky, the white of the mountain peaks and the gold of the dried grasses. There was still snow on the ground in shady areas, yet most of it was gone, especially on our Western-facing slope.

Although I haven't seen the film, the images from these two dissimilar views could create effective scenes.

Music to my ears

One late afternoon we all drove to the nearly deserted ski lodge located in Jackson, to have Dona play their piano. The piano was at the edge of the restaurant area with large windows nearby facing the ski area. Dona had not played the piano in years and wanted to practice before being filmed.

There was one lone diner in the restaurant. While we made our-selves comfortable with coffee or wine, Dona practiced her J. S. Bach. Juan Pablo and Diana discussed the question of how the background should be handled and how the lighting would be most effective. The day was quickly fading and dark permeated our space, so adjust-ments were made to create the necessary ambiance. Dona practiced on.

Vanda Scaravelli had been Dona's piano teacher as well as her yoga mentor. Vanda told her that the music is in the piano or the pose is in the body and needs to be coaxed out rather than imposed from outside. Breath and movement were also important aspects of her teaching. Vanda had been a concert pianist before her marriage. Dona enjoyed and learned a great deal from her almost-mother-daughter relationship with Vanda. Vanda, like Iyengar, was a hard taskmaster with a fun-loving nature.

Our last evening in Jackson Hole, while Dona, Diana, Karina and I were buying groceries for our last meal there, a woman at the check-out counter recognized Dona from the evening at the ski lodge. She had been that sole person in the restaurant. She thanked Dona and expressed how much she enjoyed Dona's playing during her dinner.

Such fun and suitable finale to a wonderful time.